Your role as a learning disability worker

Induction Award

Supporting people who have a learning disability

Jackie Pountney

www.bild.org.uk
✓ Information and support
✓ Useful weblinks
✓ 24 hour online ordering

0845 370 0067

www.harcourt.co.uk
✓ Free online support
✓ Useful weblinks
✓ 24 hour online ordering

01865 888118

working together **bild**

Heinemann is an imprint of Harcourt Education Limited, a company incorporated in England and Wales, having its registered office: Halley Court, Jordan Hill, Oxford OX2 8EJ. Registered company number: 3099304

www.harcourt.co.uk

Heinemann is the registered trademark of Harcourt Education Limited

Text © BILD 2007

First published 2007

12 11 10 09 08 07

10 9 8 7 6 5 4 3 2 1

British Library Cataloguing in Publication Data is available from the British Library on request.

ISBN 978 0 435500 00 9

Edited by TAG Publishing Services
Designed by 𝗧\ Tek-Art
Typeset by 𝗧\ Tek-Art, Croydon Surrey
Original illustrations © Harcourt Education Limited 2007, except for page 30 © BILD
Cover illustration © Kevin Chettle
Printed in the UK by Scotprint

Acknowledgements
The author and publisher would like to thank the following individuals and organisations for permission to reproduce photographs: Page 5 – © David J. Green – financial/Alamy; page 9 – © Harcourt Education Ltd. Martin Sookias. Mencap; pages 17, 18, 22 – © Harcourt Education Ltd. Gareth Boden; pages 26, 32 – © Janine Wiedel Photolibrary/Alamy; page 35 © Harcourt Education Ltd. Gareth Boden; page 40 – © Harcourt Education Ltd. Martin Sookias. Mencap; page 42 – © Harcourt Education Ltd. Tudor Photography; page 50 – © Ilene MacDonald/Alamy; page 55 – © Jupiter Images. Photos.com; page 63 – © Harcourt Education Ltd. Jules Selmes; page 71 – © Harcourt Education Ltd. Gareth Boden.

Every effort has been made to contact copyright holders of material reproduced in this book. Any omissions will be rectified in subsequent printings if notice is given to the publishers.

Websites
The websites used in this book were correct and up to date at the time of publication. It is essential for tutors to preview each website before using it in class so as to ensure that the URL is still accurate, relevant and appropriate. We suggest that tutors bookmark useful websites and consider enabling students to access them through the school/college/satellite centre/service provider/intranet.

Contents

About the British Institute of Learning Disabilities

The British Institute of Learning Disabilities (BILD) is committed to improving the quality of life for people with a learning disability by involving them and their families in all aspects of our work, working with government and public bodies to achieve full citizenship, undertaking beneficial research and development projects and helping service providers to develop and share good practice.

BILD Publications is the imprint of:
British Institute of Learning Disabilities
Campion House
Green Street
Kidderminster
Worcestershire DY10 1JL

Telephone: 01562 723010
Fax: 01562 723029
Email: enquiries@bild.org.uk
Website: www.bild.org.uk

BILD Publications are distributed by:
BookSource
50 Cambuslang Road
Cambuslang
Glasgow G32 8NB

Telephone: 0845 370 0067
Fax: 0845 370 0068

For a publications catalogue with details of all BILD books and journals and for information about learning and qualifications services telephone 01562 723010, email enquiries@bild.org.uk or visit the BILD website www.bild.org.uk

Acknowledgements

I would like to thank the following individuals and organisations who have given their time to help me with this book:

- Sarah, Trudy and Carol from People in Action
- Stuart, Steven, Carol, Annie, Elaine, Heather and June from Birmingham Rathbone Society
- Kate Hird from KeyRing
- Rebecca Wood from autism.west midlands
- Jane Moss
- Aseia Rafique
- Stephen Dale from Staffordshire County Council
- Autism Care UK
- Lesley Barcham from BILD

I would also like to thank Mike Bentley, Annie Lawton and Robina Mallett for reading a draft of this book and for their helpful comments and suggestions.

We gratefully acknowledge the help of Kevin Chettle for permission to reproduce his paintings on the cover and title page. The paintings are a moving account of his life in a long-stay institution. Kevin now lives in the community and earns his living through giving lectures and selling his paintings which can be purchased through Advocacy in Action, telephone 01159 470780.

About the author

Jackie Pountney has worked with people with learning disabilities for most of her working life, firstly with Birmingham Social Services Department in the early 1980s and then City College, Birmingham. When the LDAF qualification was introduced in 2001 she began to teach support workers as well. She has worked at BILD since 2004, supporting organisations to offer learning disability qualifications to their staff. She co-authored *Not behind the bikeshed*, a resource pack for teaching health and social education to people with learning disabilities, and worked with RoSPA to develop road safety training materials designed for children and adults with learning disabilities.

Introduction

induction
a period of learning, shortly after starting a new job or volunteering placement

service
the provision of social care support for a person

family carer
a relative of a person with learning disabilities

This book is for anyone beginning work with people with a learning disability. It is one of four books that will provide you with all the information you need during your **induction**. It will help you to find out more about the lives of people with learning disabilities, the **service** you work for and what it means to be a social care worker or volunteer. It will also be useful for personal assistants, volunteers and **family carers**, as well as for the growing number of people who are now managing their own support with money they receive through direct payments and individual budgets.

Learning disability qualifications

Common Induction Standards

All new workers in social care jobs need to know about a number of important topics during the first few weeks and months in their new job. What you need to know has been decided by Skills for Care, the strategic development organisation for the adult social care workforce in England. The topics have been set out in their Common Induction Standards (CIS). Your employer will provide a detailed induction programme that will cover:

- listening to people with learning disabilities and their families
- communicating effectively
- working safely
- your organisation's policies and procedures
- your role as a learning disability worker
- recognising and responding to abuse and neglect
- the principles of care.

The four induction books that cover all the CIS topics are:

- *Principles of learning disability support*
- *Your role as a learning disability worker*
- *Health and safety in a learning disability service*
- *Protecting people who have a learning disability from abuse.*

The Induction Award

As well as covering all the Skills for Care Common Induction Standards topics, the four books in this series also meet the requirements of the Induction Award: Supporting People who have a Learning Disability, a nationally recognised qualification appropriate for people who work in services that support people with learning disabilities.

The Induction Award helps new workers to develop knowledge and understanding. This series of books relating to the Common Induction Standards links to the Induction Award at levels 2 and 3.

Your role as a learning disability worker covers all the learning needed for one Induction Award unit at levels 2 and 3. Induction Award accreditiation for your induction learning will be helpful in your career in supporting people with learning disabilities because:

- you will have gained certificates for achieving a national qualification
- the knowledge and understanding gained during your induction will help you to move on to an NVQ qualification in health and social care.

NVQ in health and social care

The National Vocational Qualifications (NVQs) in health and social care are the recognised qualifications for the entire social care sector in England, Wales and Northern Ireland, including services that support people with a learning disability. In Scotland these qualifications are known as Scottish Vocational Qualifications (SVQs). NVQs assess your competence (knowledge, skills and abilities) in your job.

By completing your induction and the four Induction Award units that link to the Common Induction Standards, you will be well on the way to completing your NVQ in health and social care.

As you progress from being a new worker to a qualified and experienced worker your path of learning and qualifications could therefore look something like the diagram on the next page.

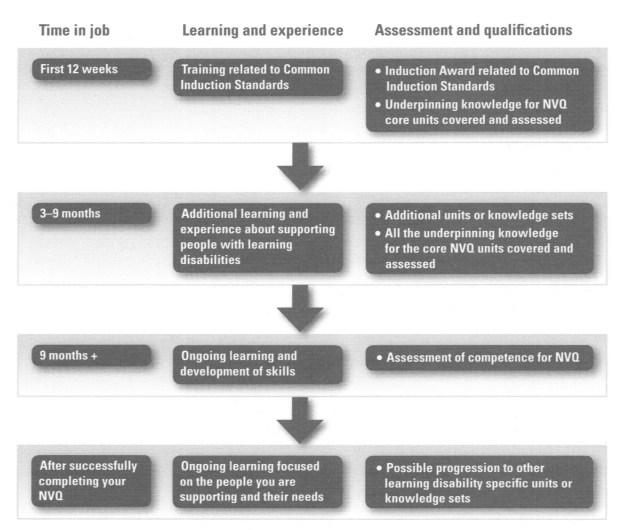

Time in job	Learning and experience	Assessment and qualifications
First 12 weeks	Training related to Common Induction Standards	• Induction Award related to Common Induction Standards • Underpinning knowledge for NVQ core units covered and assessed
3–9 months	Additional learning and experience about supporting people with learning disabilities	• Additional units or knowledge sets • All the underpinning knowledge for the core NVQ units covered and assessed
9 months +	Ongoing learning and development of skills	• Assessment of competence for NVQ
After successfully completing your NVQ	Ongoing learning focused on the people you are supporting and their needs	• Possible progression to other learning disability specific units or knowledge sets

▲ A possible path of learning and qualifications for new support workers

Working with people with learning disabilities, family carers and support workers

From day one in your work with people with learning disabilities it is important that you listen carefully to what the people you support are saying to you about their interests, needs and the support you will be providing. In researching and writing this book the author has worked closely with people with learning disabilities and has sought information about people's experiences and their views on what new workers need to know and do. Their contributions are woven throughout these books. The author has also consulted with new and experienced support workers and family carers.

Confidentiality and consent

As you work through the activities in this book, you may wish to include the person you support by, for example, talking with them about their life and using the information in an assignment. It is really important to obtain the consent of the person if you plan to include them in this way. Discuss your organisation's **confidentiality policy** with your line manager if you are unsure what to do.

Language and labels

Ideally we should call people by their name and not label them according to their age, ethnicity, religion, disability, or indeed for any other reason. We should always see the person first and not the labels that others attach to them. However, there are times when labels, no matter how much we may dislike them, are used by all of us and for all of us, for example, students, teenagers, senior citizens, patients, claimants, fans, etc.

It has been discussed for many years how we should describe people with learning disabilities. Over time, the language we use changes because terms come to have new or different meanings or because people object to the labels that are used to describe them. It is important that we are sensitive to people's concerns about the labels that others might use to describe them.

Throughout this book the terms 'people with a learning disability' or 'people with learning disabilities' are used, as these are the terms most commonly found in health and social care settings. Some organisations, including ones run by people with learning disabilities, prefer the term 'people with learning difficulties', which is also used in schools and colleges. The term 'social care worker' or 'support worker' is generally used for paid members of staff.

Those employed directly to provide social care support for people with a learning disability are generally referred to as 'personal assistants'. The word 'service' is used to refer to the workplace situation, whether this is supported living, day opportunities, community support or residential and nursing care. The word 'organisation' is used to refer to agencies that run services. Other terms that may not be clear are explained as they arise in the text or in the glossary.

confidentiality
concerning things that need to be kept private

policy
a statement or plan of action that clearly sets out an organisation's position or approach on a particular issue and tells staff what should be done in the circumstances

How this book is organised

This book is interactive. As well as reading, you will be asked to think about examples of support given to people with learning disabilities, give your own ideas, talk to colleagues and try out some of the activities.

In the next section you will find **Study skills advice** to help you get the most from the time you spend studying and help to ensure that it will be enjoyable and successful.

Each chapter contains the following features:

Learning outcomes. There are eight learning outcomes to the Your Role as a Learning Disability Worker units at levels 2 and 3 of the Induction Award: Supporting People who have a Learning Disability. They are covered in seven chapters in this book.

 Activities provide exercises designed to encourage you to apply what you have learned to your work situation.

 Key points summarise the main ideas in the chapter.

 Thinking points are suggestions for you to reflect on your own experiences and how they may affect the support you provide.

 Scenarios are brief studies illustrating ideas or issues covered in the chapter.

 Policy references give information about the key policies, laws and guidance that directly affect you as a social care worker and that set out what you have to do in your work.

 Examples provide detailed studies illustrating the key ideas covered in the chapter. These are designed to develop your ability to discuss and think more deeply about the topics as you cover them, provide an opportunity to reflect on the type of support you and your colleagues give to the people with learning disabilities you work with and give an overview of how they apply in your work on a day-to-day basis.

At the end of the book you will find the following sections:

Commentaries on the examples provides detailed feedback for the examples from the end of each chapter to help you review your work on each once it is completed.

Glossary provides explanations of technical words or phrases used in this book in plain, jargon-free English. These terms are also explained in the margin as they appear in the text.

NVQ mapping provides detailed references showing the links to NVQ health and social care qualifications.

Resources lists the key publications, DVDs and websites to refer to if you want additional information on any of the topics covered in this book.

Study skills advice

We all vary in how we study and learn. Some people prefer to study in short bursts, spreading their learning over a long period. Others prefer more sustained periods of concentration. Some of us like to study early in the day and others don't start until late in the evening. No one way of working is better than another. You should find a way that suits you. The following guidelines will help you to get the most from the time you spend studying and help to ensure that it will be enjoyable and successful.

The right environment

You will study better in a quiet room that is free from distractions and where you will be undisturbed. Make sure that your seat is comfortable and supportive and that you have enough working space to spread out your study materials. Good lighting will make reading easier and help prevent your eyes from getting tired.

Identifying and using resources

You may find some of the topics covered in this book interest you so much that you want to find out further information about them. You can find information about working with people with learning disabilities from:

- books
- newspapers
- magazines
- journals
- websites
- television
- colleagues
- people with learning disabilities.

It's a good idea to keep a record of your resources. You could cut out and keep newspaper or magazine articles and make a note of websites you have visited or television programmes you have watched. You will need to have a good filing system so that you can organise these resources to enable you to find what you need quickly.

Reading

We read for many different reasons and purposes. The reading you do for your studies is likely to be very different from reading for leisure. Probably the most important difference is the way you work through the text. When you read a novel, you will usually open it at the first page and read through to the end. This is known as 'passive reading' because you are reading everything without question. When you are studying, you may read only one chapter, or use the index to find information on one subject that is located in various places through the book. This is known as 'active reading' because you are finding the answer to a question.

When you are studying, it's a good idea to give yourself targets so that you read more effectively. You could ask yourself questions such as:

- Do I really need to know this information?
- Do I need to know some of this information?
- Is this nothing at all to do with what I need to know?

As you go through the text, have a pen near you to take notes, or a highlighter or Post-its to mark key points. This will help you to sift out information which will be useful to you.

Reading styles

Once you have established the purpose of your reading you can identify the style of reading most suited to your task. The most commonly used types of reading are:

- **Skimming** involves going through a text quickly at about two to three times your normal reading speed. Look at the index, chapter headings, introduction and conclusion, as well as looking at the first line of each paragraph. This is a useful technique for deciding whether the book contains any information that is useful to you.
- **Scanning** is useful when you know exactly what you are looking for, such as a telephone number or place name. You find the word or phrase you are looking for and then follow the text.
- **Search reading** is used to look for key words and phrases which will help you find specific information. Look in the index to see where you will find key words and topics. Then locate these in the publication by scanning though until you find the words or phrases you are interested in.
- **Receptive reading** is where you need to have a good general understanding or to find out accurately what has been written. When reading receptively you need time to pay close attention to the text, think about what you have read and perhaps make notes.

Taking notes

One of the most important skills to develop through your studies is the ability to make clear and concise notes. You can make notes in training sessions or as you read a book or article or watch a television programme. Making notes helps you to understand a topic and identify its key points.

A common mistake when taking notes is to write everything down. You can make more useful notes by thinking about what you are looking for before you start reading the material or listening to the presentation. Produce notes that are relevant only to what you are looking for and try not to be sidetracked by writing down information you don't need.

There are different ways of taking notes. You should choose a method that suits you. Bear in mind that you will have to remember what they mean later on. Some ways of taking notes are:

- a short summary of the main points
- numbered points or structured lists
- a list of headings and subheadings
- mind maps, patterns and spider diagrams
- shorthand
- key points.

You should write down where you have taken your notes from, for example, the publication or the website. If you use the information in an assignment you will need to say where you got it from. This is known as *referencing*. Use highlighter pens where you can to highlight the main points. Post-it notes are useful to mark important information that you can return to later on.

Organising your time

Spending time planning your studies can be helpful. Firstly, you can avoid a last-minute rush to meet deadlines. Secondly, if you plan how you are going to approach each task you are more likely to carry out each stage effectively and produce a higher quality piece of work. The key stages of organising your time effectively are:

- **Being realistic** is important if you want to organise your time effectively. To work out how much time you actually have to study each week you should ask yourself what other commitments you have that take up time, such as:
  - work
  - family
  - social events

- **Planning ahead** is essential. You will need to ask yourself a number of questions:
  - What exactly is involved?
  - How long will it take?
  - When will you do it?
  - How will you do it?
  - What is the deadline for completion?

- **Organising your studies** carefully will enable you to make the best use of the time you have available and help you to stay motivated and on track. Break large tasks down into manageable chunks:
  - Plan a timetable of when you will do each task.
  - Remember that it might be useful to allocate a larger amount of time to some activities. For example, writing an assignment may be better done in one session so that your ideas flow more easily.
  - Prioritise – don't do the easiest thing first, but the most immediate thing first.

Being flexible

The unexpected always happens, so don't become upset or disheartened if you are unable to stick to your timetable. Ask yourself what needs to be done to get back on track and don't be afraid to ask colleagues, family and friends to support you.

Confidentiality and consent

This book encourages you to relate what you are learning to your work situation. As part of this you will need to reflect on the way you work with people with learning disabilities. Before you involve an individual with learning disabilities in any activities from the book you will need to obtain their consent. Discuss this with your line manager before going ahead.

If you use information about or observations of your colleagues or individuals with learning disabilities in your written work you should be aware of the need for confidentiality. Rather than use someone's real name, you should use a false name or an initial to identify them. You should show the individuals what you have written or tell them about it to check that they are comfortable with what you have written. Discuss your organisation's confidentiality policy with your line manager before completing any of the activities.

Plagiarism

Passing off someone else's work as your own or using someone else's work without acknowledging them is a form of cheating known as plagiarism. Copying other people's work is a serious matter and it is not acceptable to pass off someone else's ideas as your own when you are completing any written work, such as an assignment.

Plagiarism includes:

- copying directly from a book, website, handout or another learner's work
- unfairly using another person's ideas in your work or rewriting a passage from a book or website without saying where you got the ideas from.

You can read books, handouts and information from the Internet when you are studying. To make sure you are not accused of plagiarism when writing an assignment you should always:

- complete it in your own words
- make sure, if you are studying with other people, that you each produce a different assignment
- use quotation marks if you quote directly from someone else's work – for example, 'prejudice means that we have preconceived opinions that are not based on reason'
- acknowledge fully where you obtained your information if you want to quote from a book or article or information you have obtained from the Internet – for example, give the title, author and date of publication and the publisher (for example, see page 86)
- include the web address and the date you obtained the information if you use ideas from a website (for example, see page 87).

Using the Internet

The Internet contains a wealth of information to help you with your studies. Most of it is extremely valuable. However, some websites contain information that is not reliable. Here are some things to bear in mind when using the Internet for research.

Use only websites that you know to contain reliable information. For example, if you were researching government policies you would go to an official government website. If you wanted information about a particular learning disability you would find it on the website of an organisation that supports people who have that learning disability.

Remember to note down the website address to show where you obtained the information. Do not copy information directly from a website into your own written work without saying where you got it from, as this would be a form of plagiarism.

Do not buy ready-made assignments from the Internet. This is also plagiarism.

Understanding your job

'Knowing the aims and values of the organisation is essential to delivering person-centred care. The aims and values are like the headlines. They tell us what we need to be working towards.'

Alex Jones, *Support worker*

Introduction

When you begin a new job or start work as a volunteer there is always so much to learn and find out. When you start work with people with learning disabilities it is essential that you focus on getting to know the people you are supporting. Having a good understanding of the organisation that you work for, your job and the work of your colleagues will make it easier for you to see where the day-to-day support you provide fits into the bigger picture.

A growing number of workers are supporting people with learning disabilities who receive money through **direct payments** or **individual budgets** and directly employ their own workers as personal assistants or employ personal assistants through care support agencies. Personal assistants generally only support one person. They may be part of a small team of people providing individual support, so their situation is different from workers in more traditional organisations, such as residential or day services. There are different aspects to being a learning disability worker, depending on the situation you work in.

direct payments
a way for people to organise their own social care support

individual budgets
budgets that give individuals the ability to design their own social care support and the power to decide the nature of services they need

Learning outcomes

This chapter looks at:

- understanding the aims and values of your organisation
- your role and responsibilities
- your wider responsibilities as a social care worker
- understanding other people's roles and responsibilities
- understanding policies and procedures.

The aims and values of your organisation

aims
a general statement of what an organisation hopes to achieve

values
what an organisation considers important in its work

Before looking at your own role and responsibilities, it's a good idea to look at the **aims** and **values** of your organisation. When you understand what these mean it can be easier to see how your day-to-day contribution helps your organisation work towards its goals.

An aim is a general statement of what an organisation hopes to achieve in its work with people with learning disabilities. Values are statements about what an organisation considers to be important in its work with people with learning disabilities. They are the expression of the beliefs and opinions on which the organisation was founded and underpin the way that it operates. Values inform the aims of an organisation. Some organisations put their aims into a mission statement or vision statement. Your organisation may use these terms.

Every organisation has a set of aims and values. You will have been given information about them at your interview and talked about them during your induction. Have you really thought about what they mean, and how they help you do your job?

Here are some statements about values and aims from two of the many hundreds of organisations that support people with learning disabilities. You could easily find out information about other organisations by looking at their websites or annual reviews.

Shelford Support is an organisation that offers support to people with learning disabilities. Its aims are:

- to support as many people who have a learning disability as possible to live independently
- to provide support in the way people want it when they want it
- to put an individual's own strengths and abilities at the centre of their support.

Its values are:

- All people are citizens and have the right to live as ordinary members of their community.
- All people are individuals and everyone's unique qualities, abilities and experience are valuable assets.
- People are resourceful and have the potential for developmental growth.
- People have the right to take risks and to receive support to safely exercise this choice.

Another organisation, Karling Services, says that its purpose, or aim, is:

- to support people with learning difficulties to reach their full potential and fully participate in the life of the community.

Its values are:

- All people are of equal value.
- Everyone has the potential to develop knowledge and learn new skills.
- Everyone should be allowed equal access to education, training, employment and access to the facilities in the community.

You can see from these examples that there are quite a few similarities in the values of the organisations quoted. You will also see that the aims are fairly broad. Although they do not tell us very much about the day-to-day activities of the organisation, they do give us some clues about the values that would be expected to underpin the daily work of their staff.

Thinking point
If you support an individual within their own family, think about how you could promote their values in the way you work.

Activity 1a
Values

Norah works for Karling Services, which says that one of its values is that all people are of equal worth. Norah is expected to promote this value by treating the people with learning disabilities she supports equally and with respect. List three ways that she could do this in her daily work.

person-centred plan
a way of working with people with learning disabilities that puts the person and their dreams at the centre of everything you do

support plan
a detailed plan of a person's support needs to inform the day-to-day support for that individual

If you are working as a personal assistant employed by one person, you are unlikely to have information on the aims and objectives of an organisation, but if the person wants to share them with you, you may have a copy of all or part of their **person-centred plan** or **support plan**. These should inform your values and give important information about the person's aims in life. Your work is to support them in achieving these aims.

Activity 1b
Aims and values

Find and read a copy of the aims and values of your organisation. List three ways that you can promote its aims and values through your day-to-day work. When you have completed this activity, discuss it with your line manager or supervisor.

Key point
Knowing the aims and values of your organisation helps you to understand what the organisation will expect of you as an employee.

Your role and responsibilities

Your role and responsibilities are set out in your **job description** and your job title will indicate the type of work you do. You should, in addition, have a personal development plan that will enable you to progress in your work.

Your job title

Some job titles describe the job very clearly. For example, website designer, nurse, bricklayer and librarian make it obvious what is expected. But other job titles, such as analyst, materials handler and production operative, while giving some idea of the type of work undertaken, are not specific enough to tell you in which sector (e.g. health, education, finance) the work is done, let alone what day-to-day tasks are involved.

Your job title in learning disability can fall into either group, although it should give you some idea of what your job involves. For example, what do these job titles tell you about the job?

- Support worker
- Home carer
- Personal assistant
- Care assistant

These titles tell you something about the job, but not too much. Two people with the same job title may in fact do very similar work, or their work may be very different.

Your job description

When you applied for your job as a learning disability worker you should have received a job description. When you started in your current role your line manager, the person you are supporting or your employer should have gone through your job description with you in detail. A job description gives information about:

- the different activities you will be doing with people with learning disabilities, and possibly their family
- your responsibilities
- who you are accountable to.

Although job descriptions can vary from organisation to organisation, or from person to person, and some may still not be very detailed, your job description is an important document for you in your new role as a learning disability worker.

job description
a document that gives detailed information about your work, what you will be doing, who you are responsible to, etc.

Thinking point
What is your job title? Does it describe what you do?

Activity 1c

Job description

Find your job description and any other information you have about your job. If you don't have a job description ask your line manager for a copy. Read through the information carefully and write down the key words and phrases that relate to the three different aspects of your job outlined above.

Discuss what you have written with your line manager or the person you support. Use the discussion to clarify any areas you are unclear about and to get more information on areas that are vague.

If you are a volunteer you are unlikely to have a job description, but you may well have a written task or role description which should contain some or all of the following elements:

- your title
- the purpose of your role
- who you are responsible to
- the activities or tasks you will be involved in.

The task description could also include additional information on the time and location of your volunteering, as well as any policies you may be asked to adhere to, such as on confidentiality or health and safety. Many organisations now have a volunteers' Code of Conduct. If the organisation you work with has one, make sure you have read it through and had an opportunity to discuss what it means for you in the voluntary work you undertake.

Thinking point
What is your job title? Does it describe what you do?

▲ As a learning disability worker, you should have received a job description.

Your personal development plan

To ensure that you have the skills necessary to do your job effectively as outlined in the job description, you may be asked to identify, with your manager, a programme of training that will enable you to acquire new skills for career development.

Your wider responsibilities as a social care worker

As well as having responsibilities towards the people you support and the organisation that employs you, you also have wider responsibilities as one of over a million social care workers in the UK. The social care councils for each of the four countries of the UK were set up by the government in 2001 to register and regulate all social care workers. The **General Social Care Council**, the Care Council for Wales, The Northern Ireland Social Care Council and the Scottish Social Services Council all published *Codes of Practice for Social Care Workers* in 2002.

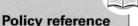

You should always work to the standards set out in the ***Code of Practice***. They set out standards relating to professional conduct and practice that are required of social care workers. You will find that many of these are similar to those from your own organisation, but the difference is that these are set at a national level and have been devised to ensure people who are supported, their families, carers and other members of the public know the standards of conduct they should expect from social care workers.

The *Code of Practice* for England says that social care workers must:

- protect the **rights** and promote the interests of service users and carers
- strive to establish and maintain the trust and confidence of service users and carers
- promote the independence of service users while protecting them as far as possible from danger or harm
- respect the rights of service users while seeking to ensure that their behaviour does not harm themselves or other people.

The *Code of Practice* also states that, as a social care worker, you must protect the rights and promote the interests of service users and carers. This includes:

- treating each person as an individual
- respecting and, where appropriate, promoting the individual views and wishes of both service users and carers

General Social Care Council

the organisation that regulates the social care workforce in England

Code of Practice

a UK document for social care workers setting out the standards they should be working to

Policy reference

Code of Practice for Social Care Workers General Social Care Council for England (2002)

Code of Practice for Employers of Social Care Workers General Social Care Council for England (2002)

rights

a framework of laws that protects people from harm and guarantees them basic entitlements, such as the right to respect, equality, and a fair trial

- supporting service users' rights to control their lives and make informed choices about the services they receive
- respecting and maintaining the dignity and privacy of service users
- promoting equal opportunities for service users and carers
- respecting diversity and different cultures and values.

Scenario: Paul and Michael's holiday

Julia has been asked to help two people she supports plan a holiday. Although they are good friends and they want to go on holiday together, they have very different personalities. Paul likes the peace and quiet of the countryside, while Michael loves the noise and nightlife of a resort. Julia's role is to help them to plan a holiday that caters for both their tastes.

Your own job role and responsibilities will be more specific than those described in the *Code of Practice* above, but they are underpinned by the values and aims of the organisation you work for, as well as your responsibilities as a social care worker, like this:

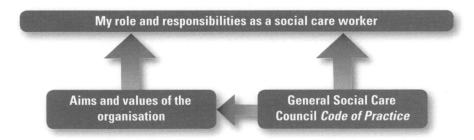

▲ Your job role and responsibilities are underpinned by the values and aims of your organisation and by your responsibilities as a social care worker.

You will have been given information about your role and responsibilities at your interview and during your induction to your new job. However, you are bound to find yourself in situations in which you are unclear about the limits of your own responsibility, and you need help and advice from others.

Getting advice, information and support

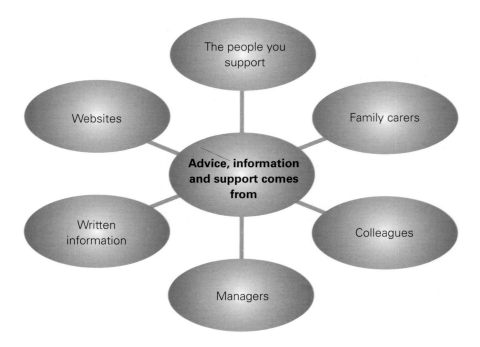

▲ Advice, information and support can come from many different sources.

As a new worker or volunteer you are not expected to know everything about your role or the organisation you work for immediately. One of the exciting things about being a learning disability worker is that you will meet new situations and experiences all the time. Don't be afraid to seek advice, information and support when you need it. These could come from six main sources:

- **The people you support** are in the best position to comment on the kind of support they need. They may also have lots of information and knowledge about other things, such as their own disability, wider issues in the learning disability community and events or activities in the local community that they would like to access.
- **Family carers** usually have a wealth of information about the person you are supporting and most are very willing to share information with new support workers.
- **Colleagues** can provide a wealth of experience and advice as well as emotional support in difficult situations.
- **Managers** can provide information and advice about policies and **procedures** in your organisation, your job description and role and about your work setting. Don't be afraid to seek support from your manager in difficult situations.

procedures
a set of instructions setting out in detail how a policy should be implemented and what staff should do in response to a specific situation

- **Written information**, such as policies, procedures and the aims and values of your organisation, can be found in the staff handbook which you may have received during your induction. Make sure you are familiar with this document and know where to find the information you may need in the future. Your organisation may also hold these documents on its Intranet. If you need general information on wider learning disability issues you may find it in your organisation's library. Alternatively, you can contact organisations, such as BILD, that provide information for new workers (see Resources section).
- **Websites** are a source of information for people who have access to a computer and the Internet either through work, at home or through their local library. A vast amount of information is available on the Internet, but you need to be careful that it is accurate and current. One way of doing this is to make sure that the site you get information from is trustworthy. Some reputable websites are listed in the Resources section to get you started.

▲ The people you support are in the best position to comment on the kind of support they need.

Scenario: How is Karen feeling?

Karen has a profound learning disability and cannot communicate verbally. She lives at home with her family. When Adele started a new role as Karen's support worker she was not always able to tell from her gestures and sounds how Karen was feeling. Although she felt awkward at first, she plucked up the courage to ask Karen's mother for advice. Karen's mother was delighted to tell her how to interpret Karen's gestures and sounds. Now Adele knows Karen very well and is able to tell others how Karen is feeling.

Thinking point

Do you know how many people are employed by your organisation and service? If you have other colleagues, how well do you understand their roles and responsibilities?

Understanding other people's roles and responsibilities

If you work as a personal assistant (PA) to a person with a learning disability who receives a direct payment or an individual budget, you will generally only be supporting one person and there may only be one or two other PAs working with that person. However, there may well be other people supporting the person, such as their relatives or health professionals, and you will need to know about the support they provide.

Some support workers work in organisations that have several hundred workers and support a large number of people with a learning disability. These large organisations are usually divided into different services, each covering a particular area.

Activity 1d
Other people's roles and responsibilities

Think about how to understand other people's roles and responsibilities. Imagine you have to introduce a visitor to someone from your staff group or someone who also supports the same person as you, or who has a different job from you, but is not your line manager. How would you explain their roles and responsibilities?

Remember the issue of confidentiality when working on this activity and be sure to seek the consent of the person you support to undertake this work.

Understanding policies and procedures

Most organisations have policies and procedures that describe the right way to carry out particular tasks. Policies set out an organisation's position on particular issues and offer guidance on what to do. Procedures give practical guidance on how the policies should be implemented and explain what staff should do in response to a specific situation.

So, for example, your organisation will have a policy on confidentiality. This will explain the reasons for confidentiality and the organisation's commitment to maintaining confidential information. The procedures will show staff and others how they are to deliver the policy in their daily work. For example, the procedures will tell you:

- what information you can give to others
- how you must store records and files
- what to do in case of a breach of confidentiality.

Policies and procedures can usually be found in the staff handbook. If your organisation has an Intranet, copies of policies and procedures can often be downloaded from there. Every member of staff should have a copy, or should know where a copy is kept. Supervisors and managers need to be sure that every member of staff is aware of all the policies and procedures relating to their work. As a new member of staff, it is your job to find out about policies and procedures and to check with your manager if there is anything you don't fully understand.

Thinking point

Have you ever been in a situation where confidential information about you was passed on without your permission? What happened? How did you feel?

Activity 1e

Policies and procedures

Find a complete list of all your organisation's policies and procedures and write down all those that relate directly to your new job.

Talk to your line manager or supervisor about the list you have made and make sure you ask about anything you don't understand.

Key point

It is your responsibility to be sure you fully understand all the policies and procedures that relate to your work.

To demonstrate that you have understood the information about the importance of knowing the aims and values of your organisation, and of following policies and procedures, you should be able to discuss why they are important when supporting people who have a learning disability. The following example should help you do this.

Example 1: Policies and procedures

Hannah is a young woman in her mid-twenties who has a moderate learning disability. She lives alone in a flat and receives three hours of assistance from a support worker each day. Hannah is very sociable, and has a wide circle of friends and acquaintances. One night, Hannah has a party in her flat, which is attended by a small group of friends. The following morning Hannah is concerned because she has lost her ring. It is a family heirloom that was handed on to her by her late mother. Hannah is very distressed. She is sure that she had put the ring down safely somewhere, but cannot remember where. When Maureen, her support worker, arrives later that morning Hannah tells her about losing the ring. Maureen helps her to search for it but, when she too is unable to find it, she explains to Hannah that she has to follow the organisation's procedure for reporting an incident. She completes an incident report form and informs her manager. Later that day, as part of the organisation's policies and procedures, the police visit Hannah and Maureen stays with her. The ring is never found.

1. What challenges did Maureen face?
2. Do you think Maureen was right to follow the organisation's policy for reporting an incident?
3. What should Maureen have done if Hannah hadn't wanted to report the incident in line with the policy and procedures?
4. Did Maureen breach Hannah's right to confidentiality?
5. Discuss this example with your line manager. How would people in your organisation manage a situation like this? How would you use your policies and procedures in a similar situation?

Now turn to the commentary on this example on page 77.

Working in partnership

2

> 'Most family carers want to work with support workers to give the best possible support to their relative. They want support workers to treat them with respect and to listen to them.'
>
> Angie Robinson, *Family carer*

Introduction

In your work you will probably come into contact with a wide variety of people at different times. Obviously, your main relationship is with the person with a learning disability who you support, but you may also work with members of the person's family, their friends, other support workers and professionals and people in the person's wider circle of contacts, such as those where they work or at leisure and social activities.

Partnership working will be important in your work. There are different approaches to working in partnership with others who are significant to the person you support and with other workers and professionals.

Learning outcomes

This chapter looks at:

- understanding the roles of others
- the importance of working in partnership
- attitudes and approaches that help partnership working.

Understanding the roles of others

When you begin your new role supporting a person with a learning disability, you may find that there are a variety of people who also support the same person, but in different ways. These could include members of their family and friends, as well as professionals and other workers. It is important that you understand the roles and responsibilities of all those involved in the person's life and the different relationships that you will need to establish with them.

Activity 2a

People in your life

Think about the range of people involved in your life and the kinds of relationship you have with them. Draw a picture of yourself in the middle of a sheet of paper and put information about these people on the sheet, listing them in groups such as family, loved ones, close friends, friends, colleagues and people who support you.

Ask the person you support to do the same, explaining to them what the activity is about and why you are doing it. Talk to them about their life and the people who are important to them. If you are working with someone who doesn't use speech to communicate you may find it helpful to get support from their family and friends and look at any life story books they may have.

Working together, draw a picture of the person or write their name down in the middle of a sheet of paper. Think of everyone who is directly involved in the person's life and write their names on the paper as well, noting down the role of each person next to their name. Now compare the two diagrams. What are the differences? Why do these differences occur? You may find the diagrams look something like the ones below.

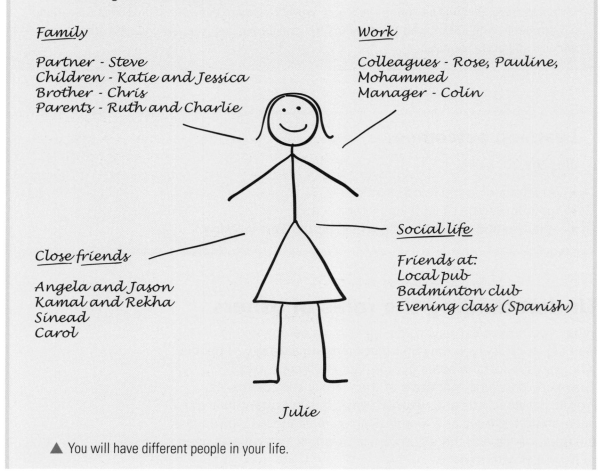

Family

Partner - Steve
Children - Katie and Jessica
Brother - Chris
Parents - Ruth and Charlie

Work

Colleagues - Rose, Pauline, Mohammed
Manager - Colin

Social life

Friends at:
Local pub
Badminton club
Evening class (Spanish)

Close friends

Angela and Jason
Kamal and Rekha
Sinead
Carol

Julie

▲ You will have different people in your life.

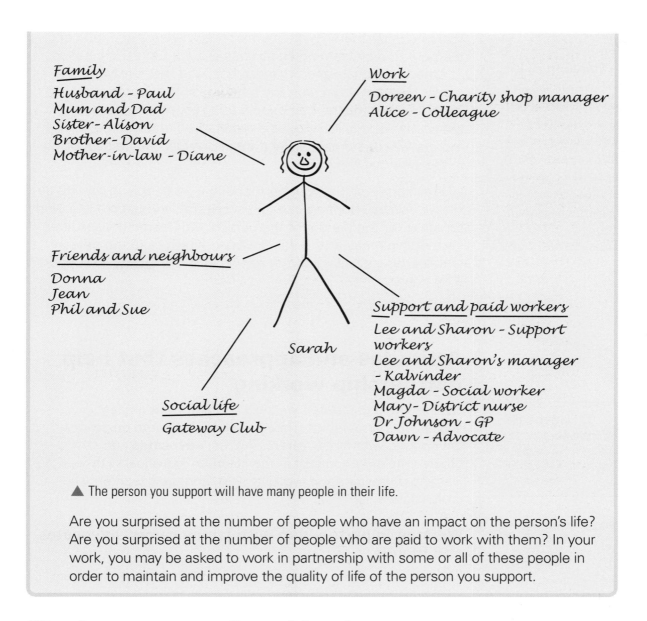

Family
Husband - Paul
Mum and Dad
Sister- Alison
Brother- David
Mother-in-law - Diane

Work
Doreen - Charity shop manager
Alice - Colleague

Friends and neighbours
Donna
Jean
Phil and Sue

Sarah

Support and paid workers
Lee and Sharon - Support workers
Lee and Sharon's manager - Kalvinder
Magda - Social worker
Mary - District nurse
Dr Johnson - GP
Dawn - Advocate

Social life
Gateway Club

▲ The person you support will have many people in their life.

Are you surprised at the number of people who have an impact on the person's life? Are you surprised at the number of people who are paid to work with them? In your work, you may be asked to work in partnership with some or all of these people in order to maintain and improve the quality of life of the person you support.

The importance of working in partnership

In Activity 2a you will probably have come up with quite a long list of organisations and people who contribute to the support of individuals you work with. In the past these people and services did not often work in partnership, but in isolation from each other. They may not have communicated with each other. They may have used jargon and followed policies and procedures that were particular to their own profession. It would have been up to the individual with learning disabilities and their family to find out about these organisations and get help from them. In practice, this meant that many individuals and their families became frustrated, gave up trying and often had poor quality or inadequate support.

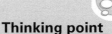

Working in partnership means that the wishes and needs of the person with learning disabilities are put before the needs of other individuals and organisations, and that everyone works together to provide the best possible support. Working in partnership means that people bring together different knowledge and skills and, as a result, problems can be solved more easily and creatively and the individual can be supported in the way that they want.

Thinking point
Have you and your family and friends ever had to work together to resolve a conflict or sort out a problem? Was it successful? If something went wrong, why do you think this happened?

Like all partnerships, your partnership with people in the life of the person you support can be successful, and people can work together for the benefit of the person with learning disabilities. Partnerships may also break down, in which case the person with learning disabilities may not receive the quality of support they need.

Attitudes and approaches that help partnership working

advocate
an independent person who supports someone to speak up for themselves

The following guidelines will help you see what makes successful partnerships. They have been split into guidelines for working with family carers, friends, **advocates** and others who are important in the life of an individual with learning disabilities and working with other paid workers and professionals.

Working in partnership with family carers, advocates and friends

For support workers, working in partnership with family carers, advocates and friends means:

Key point
Working in partnership with family carers, advocates and friends of the people you support means respecting their expertise and commitment, promoting good communication and understanding their perspective.

- involving the person with a learning disability, unless there is a risk to them or others from working in this way
- recognising, encouraging and maintaining relationships where they exist
- recognising and respecting each other's knowledge and expertise in relation to the person with learning disabilities
- communicating openly and clearly with each other and listening carefully to what others say
- working constructively to overcome any differences of view or opinion that may exist for the benefit of the person with a learning disability.

▲ Working in partnership with family carers, friends and advocates means listening carefully to what others say.

Working in partnership with other professionals

For support workers, working in partnership with colleagues and other professionals means:

- sharing a commitment to providing person-centred support for the person
- being clear about decisions that are made and the reasons for them
- learning about and respecting other people's roles and responsibilities
- taking account of opinions and ideas that are different from your own
- refusing to take part in any situation you recognise as 'unprofessional'
- recognising that you are a member of a team of people with different strengths and talents and being confident in your own worth and ability, while not undermining anyone else
- dealing immediately and directly with any injustice done to you or a colleague or any unprofessional behaviour.

Key point
Working in partnership with colleagues means respecting the roles and views of others, communicating clearly and openly, sharing a commitment to supporting the individual in a person-centred way and constructively challenging poor practice where necessary.

▲ Working in partnership with colleagues means taking account of opinions and ideas that are different from your own.

The example below gives an idea of how support workers are working in partnership in their day-to-day support of people with learning disabilities.

Working in partnership		
Partnership example	**Who the support worker is working in partnership with**	**How they are promoting good partnership working**
Sadiq has recently been diagnosed with diabetes. Paul, his support worker, accompanies him to his first appointment with the diabetes nurse at the surgery.	• Sadiq • the diabetes nurse	• Focusing on Sadiq and his needs
The nurse explains to Sadiq about the foods he should be eating to keep healthy. Paul works with Sadiq and the nurse to explore how best to explain to Sadiq and his family about Sadiq's diet and the medication he should take.	• Sadiq • Sadiq's family	• Sharing information • Respecting each other's experience and expertise • Agreeing a shared plan of action

To demonstrate that you have understood the information about partnership working, you should be able to discuss good practice in partnership working. The following example should help you do this.

Example 2: Partnership working

Andrew is an experienced support worker. He has recently started to work with Lucy and Paul, a married couple. They are both described as having learning disabilities and live in supported accommodation. The first time he meets them, Lucy's parents are visiting them and everyone is distressed. Lucy has shown her mother their bank statement and they have found that they are £1,000 overdrawn. The bank statement is not in a form that Lucy and Paul can easily understand. When he investigates further, Andrew finds that they are overdrawn because Paul's benefits have been stopped, although Paul was unaware of this.

Over the next few weeks and months Paul and Andrew get in touch with the benefits agency to find out why benefits have been stopped. They manage to get them reinstated and arrears paid. Lucy and Paul visit the bank with

continued ▶

Andrew and they arrange to have their statements sent to them in a form that they understand. Andrew spends time working with Lucy and her parents together to rebuild their confidence that Lucy and Paul can live independently.

1. List the organisations and individuals that Andrew has worked with in order to support Lucy and Paul during this crisis.

2. What skills do you think Andrew will have used when working in partnership with these people?

3. How did Andrew empower Lucy and Paul to be part of resolving their financial issues?

Now turn to the commentary on this example on page 78.

Your responsibilities as a support worker

> 'Being a support worker for me is not just about being Wallie's friend. It's more than that. I need to be professional in everything I do.'
>
> Blossom Adeyu, *Support worker*

Introduction

When we start a new role we usually like to know what we need to do and how to behave in order to do a good job. As a support worker you have important new responsibilities to the people you support, which include being reliable and dependable. However, you also need to bear in mind the limitations of your role as there are some actions or behaviours that you should avoid because they are at best inappropriate or at worst unacceptable.

Learning outcomes

This chapter looks at:

- your relationship with the person you support
- what is meant by a professional relationship
- actions or behaviour that would be unacceptable towards someone you support.

Your relationship with the person you support

In some ways your relationship with the person you support will be similar to other relationships in your life. For example, you may get on with some people very well, while you may find others harder to like. The people you support may also get on well with some support workers and not very well with others. However, in other ways these relationships will be very different.

People with learning disabilities are often socially excluded. This means they often have fewer opportunities to do things that are important to other people, such as have paid employment or use leisure facilities in their local area. They may be less likely to have contact with their families than people without learning disabilities, and they may not see their friends as regularly.

Thinking point

Are any of your colleagues also friends who you see socially outside work? Do you behave differently with them when you are at work? If there is a problem at work, does it affect your friendship?

Many people with learning disabilities spend a substantial amount of time with people who are paid to be with them and may share a lot of personal information with them. One result of this is that many individuals with learning disabilities regard the people who support them as their friends. While this may be flattering for you as a support worker, and may help you both to have a good relationship, you should remember that you also have a professional relationship with the people you support.

Having a professional relationship with a person with learning disabilities who you support means:

- respecting and valuing them even if you find it difficult to like them
- trying not to let your own feelings and prejudices get in the way of your work
- listening to people and trying to understand their perspective
- recognising and upholding the rights of every person with learning disabilities
- responding appropriately and sensitively to people's needs and demands, while helping them to recognise and accept their responsibilities

▲ Having a professional relationship with a person with learning disabilities who you support means working *with* the person and not doing everything *for* them.

- working *with* the person and not doing everything *for* them or taking over all responsibilities
- not patronising people or criticising them in public or behind their backs
- recognising people's right to control their own lives, as long as it does not affect the freedom of others
- remembering you have a duty of care towards the people you support.

Scenario: Supporting Andrew to go swimming

Andrew loves swimming and his visit to the local pool is the highlight of his week. His key worker Steve usually goes with him, but when Steve is on holiday it is part of Laura's job to support him instead. Laura does not like swimming and she particularly dislikes going swimming with Andrew because he splashes her. Although she dislikes this part of her day, Laura knows how important swimming is to Andrew so she hides her feelings.

It's important that you develop a good relationship with the person you support, as this relationship is crucial to providing good quality support. Good communication is a key element of developing a good working relationship between you and the person you support. In chapters 4 and 5 we explore in more detail how you can build good relationships on the foundation of good communication.

Your relationship with the person you support is different from other relationships because you:

- are employed to provide support and your contract of employment sets out in detail the nature of that support
- have a duty of care
- are bound by a professional *Code of Practice for Social Care Workers*
- will move in and out of the person's life.

Although as members of society we all have a general 'duty of care' to others, you have additional responsibilities in relation to your 'duty of care' as a support worker.

Among other things, a 'duty of care' means you will do your best to ensure people's safety, keep accurate records, keep information and records confidential, keep your knowledge and skills up to date and only accept work delegated to you that you are competent to undertake.

Thinking point
What does your general 'duty of care' as a member of society mean in practice? How do you think it differs from the 'duty of care' you have in your role as a learning disability worker?

Diagram centre: **A duty of care means**

- Respecting diversity and difference
- Working in a person-centred way
- Supporting individual choice and decision-making
- Promoting good communication
- Sharing power
- Upholding the rights of everyone you work with

▲ You have a duty of care toward the people you support.

A professional relationship

The *Codes of Practice for Social Care Workers* say that, as a social care worker, you must strive to establish and maintain the trust and confidence of the people you support and carers and that this includes being reliable and dependable.

We depend on other people and we rely on them in many areas of our daily life. For example, we depend on the newsagent to have our daily paper first thing in the morning and on the rail company for our train to work. We rely on the local supermarket to have apples when we go in to buy them and depend on members of our family to make our daily routine go smoothly, as well as for support in bigger issues. We also rely on each other to be honest and caring and for support when we are ill or are having a difficult time at work.

You can probably remember times when other people who you have relied on haven't done what they said they would do. Maybe they forgot, or were delayed, or maybe they tried to do something and were let down by others. You probably felt upset or angry that they didn't do what they said they would do. If it's only a minor matter you are probably able to find a way round the issue, such as buying your paper from another shop or buying pears instead of apples. Sometimes, if it's something really important and you and others are inconvenienced and hurt, your trust in that person is broken.

If people or organisations are reliable and do what they agree to do, we develop a relationship of trust with them and feel more confident about asking them for assistance or for their services. If, however, people let us down or organisations fail to provide the service we expect, we are less likely to use them in the future. It's just the same in your work with people with learning disabilities. The support you provide is often essential to the person and their family. If you are dependable, they will feel more able to trust you and rely on you.

You may find it helpful to talk to the people you support and their families about what being dependable actually means to them and why they think it is important. In your day-to-day work, being reliable usually means:

- arriving for work at the right time and in the right place
- doing your best to do something you have agreed to do or letting people know as soon as possible if you are unable to do it
- not leaving early or taking long breaks
- letting people know as soon as possible if you are sick and unable to work.

Thinking point

Have you ever been let down by someone who promised to do something and then failed to do it? Perhaps you have waited in all day for someone to repair your washing machine, or deliver something, and they did not turn up. How did you feel?

▲ It is important to respect the person you are supporting and to think about their needs before your own.

Unacceptable actions or behaviour

If you were asked to give examples of actions or behaviour towards the people you support that are unacceptable, you would probably think they were obvious. You might say that it is unacceptable to hit someone, swear at them, steal from them or abuse them physically, emotionally or sexually. Of course all of these are unacceptable, but there are many less obvious examples of unacceptable actions or behaviour.

Think about the setting in which you work. It may be in an individual's own home, in a family home, in the local community, in a residential home or in a day centre. In each setting it's important to remember to work in a person-centred way, and to put the needs and wishes of the person who you are supporting before your own. For example, if you are supporting an individual in their own home, it would be unacceptable to go and make yourself a drink or snack unless you were invited to do so. It would not be acceptable to use the telephone without asking permission first. Some organisations have policies on using the telephone of the people you support and would say it was always unacceptable. If the individual you support wants to undertake an activity which you don't particularly enjoy or you don't feel like doing at the time, it would be unacceptable to try to influence their decision.

▲ Working in a person-centred way means putting the needs and wishes of the person you support first.

Other examples of unacceptable behaviour are:

- not keeping personal information confidential
- putting people in potentially risky or dangerous situations
- borrowing money or any possessions from the person you support.

Scenario: Showing respect for Greg

Rita is supporting Greg to cook his lunch. While she is working with him, her mobile phone rings. Without apologising to Greg for answering the phone, she starts to plan a night out with her friend. Greg has to wait for her to finish her conversation before he can continue to prepare his lunch. Unknown to Rita, her line manager Winston has observed this from the door. When they are alone later, Winston explains that Rita has shown a lack of respect for Greg. He should not have been kept waiting to complete the task while Rita chatted and she should not be taking personal calls while she is working.

You should aim to promote the duties set out in the *Codes of Practice for Social Care Workers* in everything you do. If you are at all unsure about any actions you are thinking of undertaking at work, you should always check with your line manager before going ahead.

Key point
It is important to work in a person-centred way and to ensure that the needs and wishes of the person you support come before your own.

Activity 3a

Unacceptable actions and behaviour

Ask a person you support, a colleague and your line manager what they think are unacceptable actions or behaviour towards a person with learning disabilities. Make a list of five unacceptable behaviours or actions. Against each one write how you think support workers should behave. Discuss the list and your ideas with your line manager or a senior colleague.

To demonstrate that you have understood the information about your responsibilities towards the people you support, you should be able to discuss what it means to have a professional relationship with them. The following example should help you do this.

Example 3: Professional relationships

Craig lives in a residential home with three other people. He is described as having severe learning disabilities, uses a wheelchair and doesn't communicate verbally. Support workers Manjula and James accompany Craig to the local shops to buy his magazine. James pushes the wheelchair along the pavement and tells Manjula about an incident that happened the previous day with another resident. Neither Manjula nor James speaks to Craig. When they arrive at the shops, James leaves Manjula and Craig and goes into the supermarket to buy some food for his supper which he will have when he finishes work. Manjula takes Craig into the newsagent. She takes the magazine that Craig usually has from the shelf and puts it in his hand. She wheels Craig to the till and pays for the magazine. They leave the shop and wait outside for James to join them to walk back to Craig's home. Manjula and James are chatting and laughing, but not with Craig. Craig sits quietly, looking around him and holding his magazine.

1. Do you think Manjula and James have a professional relationship with Craig?

2. List three positive aspects of their relationship with Craig.

3. Make a list of the actions or behaviours that are unacceptable in this example.

4. How could James and Manjula work in a more professional way with Craig?

5. Discuss your ideas with your line manager. Explain how you would support Craig in a professional way.

Now turn to the commentary on this example on page 78.

Factors that affect communication

4

'David might not be able to speak, but he has lots of other ways of letting us know what he wants.'

Sarah Britton, *Family carer*

Introduction

Every day we interact with other people in a number of different situations for a whole variety of reasons. Most of the time we express ourselves and listen to others with ease and don't think twice about the complexity of day-to-day communication. People with learning disabilities often find understanding and using both verbal and non-verbal communication challenging. It is up to us to adjust the way we communicate, so that the people we support can take the lead, get their own messages across and understand what we say.

Learning outcomes

This chapter covers:

- what motivates people to communicate
- barriers to communication
- how a person's behaviour may be a way of communicating their needs, feelings, choices or views.

What motivates people to communicate

Communication is vital to us as human beings. It enables us to interact with others and make sense of what's going on around us. We communicate to:

- meet our physical needs (e.g. we may be hungry or thirsty, too cold or too warm, feel tired and want to rest)
- meet our emotional and social needs (e.g. form and cement relationships and express our feelings)
- exchange information and learn new things (e.g. know why something is being done)
- express our spiritual needs (e.g. attend religious services).

If we are unable to communicate, we can feel misunderstood, frustrated, isolated, excluded and anxious.

Effective communication

For communication to be effective, a person must use all the means at their disposal to make sure that they send a clear message. The receiver must listen carefully in order to understand the message and relate it to the knowledge and experience they already have. Communication may not finish there, of course, as the roles can be reversed, with the receiver responding by sending a message and the original sender becoming the receiver. If another person joins in, the process becomes more complex.

In our work with people with learning disabilities, both verbal and non-verbal communication are of vital importance. Working with a person who doesn't use words to communicate can be daunting for new workers, but the diagram below shows you just how little of our communication is through words and how much meaning is conveyed in other ways.

8% What we say
● words/phrases

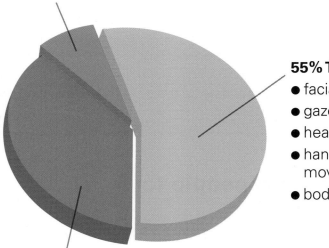

55% Things we see
● facial expression
● gaze pattern
● head movements
● hand/arm/leg movements
● body positioning

37% How we sound
● rate
● volume
● stress/intonation
● pitch
● fluency

▲ How we communicate.

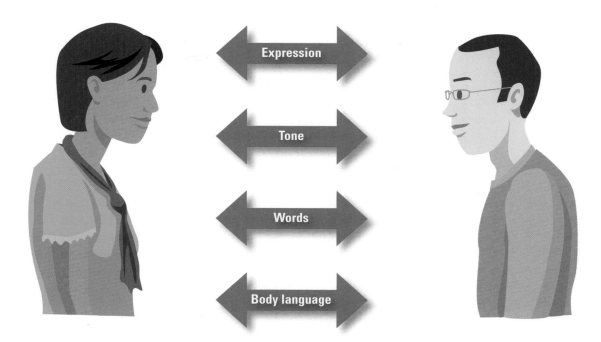

▲ There are different elements to communication – not just the words that are spoken.

Knowing that facial expression, body language and tone of voice can carry meaning will help you find ways to understand what the person you are supporting is saying. Understanding the importance of your own non-verbal communication can also help you in your work with people with learning disabilities.

Barriers to communication

Have you ever been on holiday to a country where you couldn't speak, understand or read the language? You may have had difficulty ordering a meal in a restaurant, because you couldn't understand the menu and the waiters didn't speak English. Because you couldn't speak or understand the local language you may have felt excluded from much of what was going on around you and only been able to talk to people who spoke your language.

Communication barriers usually arise because there is a breakdown in understanding between the person who is sending the message and those who are meant to be receiving it. Communication barriers can be within the social environment of the person, in their physical environment or occur because of personal disabilities or experiences.

Thinking point
Do you ever watch people in a public place talking, and try to guess what their relationship is? Even if you can't hear what they are saying you can often tell if they are enjoying themselves or having an argument by their body language and facial expressions.

Social barriers

Day-to-day social situations may make it difficult for a person with learning disabilities to communicate effectively. Many of these barriers are caused by the attitudes of the people working with them. They can be overcome if support workers think about the way they work and are creative in the way they support people. The table opposite includes some of the more common barriers in the social environment for people with learning disabilities and how they can be overcome.

Physical barriers

Sometimes we don't think enough about how the physical environment can affect the person who is trying to communicate with us. There are some situations where it's more difficult to communicate. The table opposite identifies a number of potentially difficult communication situations and what you can do to support communication in these situations.

▲ Choose a quiet environment to communicate in.

Social barriers to communication	
Social barriers to communication	**How to overcome social barriers to communication**
Low expectations People's expectations are often so low that they don't involve people with learning disabilities in conversations, thinking they will be unable to understand.	**Raise your expectations** Support workers should always expect and support communication with the people they support.
Lack of time Sometimes we use time as an excuse. We say there is just not enough time to listen to people and don't give them time to communicate adequately. We assume the person can't express themselves, and we say everything for them.	**Give the person you support time to communicate** Never interrupt the person you are supporting and always give them the time they need to complete what they want to say. This shows respect for the person and what they want to communicate.
Lack of focus Sometimes we are so preoccupied with our own affairs that we don't attend to what someone is trying to tell us. We often ignore a person's attempts to communicate. Other times we hear what is being said, but don't really listen or concentrate on what this means for the person concerned.	**Be person centred** Being person centred is important every day in your support of a person with a learning disability. You should respect the person you support and promote their views and wishes, not your own.

Physical barriers to communication	
Physical barriers to communication	**How to overcome physical barriers to communication**
Discomfort Being in a place where a person with a learning disability feels uncomfortable may be distracting. It may be too hot or cold or just be a place where they are ill at ease.	**Find a comfortable place** With the person you support, identify places where they feel most comfortable. These will be the best places to communicate effectively.
Noise Being in an environment where there's lots of background noise, such as from piped music, other people talking and telephones ringing can make it difficult to hear what people are saying.	**Choose a quiet environment** Use your observation skills as well as asking the person how they feel about communicating in noisy places. Be led by them in identifying the best places to communicate.
High activity Being where there are lots of people around and lots of activity can be distracting and make it more difficult for people to communicate.	**Find a calm atmosphere** Some people love crowds and others hate them. Being person centred in your approach to communication will mean that you will be seeking to find out what the person you support really prefers.
Stress Being in some situations, such as a one-to-one 'interview' situation, can be stressful.	**Create a stress-free environment** People find some places stressful and feel more anxious communicating in those places. Once you know the situations the person you support finds stressful you can avoid them.

Activity 4a

Communication barriers

Think of a person with learning disabilities you know well and the possible communication barriers they may face.

List three possible social barriers that may prevent them from communicating effectively. Against each barrier note down one way you could help to overcome the barriers.

List three possible physical barriers that may prevent them from communicating effectively. Against each barrier note down one way you could help to break down the barriers.

You may find it useful to discuss this activity with the person with a learning disability or another person who knows them well. Try out the steps you have identified and see if they make a difference.

Personal barriers

People with learning disabilities can have difficulties with communication that arise because of their disability or from their experiences so far. For example, they may:

- not have the words they need to express themselves
- be unable to use sentences that are long enough to explain what they want to say
- have difficulty with pronunciation
- be unable to speak
- have a hearing difficulty that is not being properly treated and be unable to hear what is being said to them properly
- have a visual impairment and be unable to see the people they are communicating with clearly and so miss out on important non-verbal communication
- not fully understand the meaning of a conversation because it is too quick or complicated
- feel intimidated and clam up in stressful situations or have had negative experiences of being ignored and not listened to
- not understand the slang or jargon that is used
- not understand the accent or dialect of the person who is speaking to them.

Key point

Lack of understanding of people's life experiences, low expectations, time pressures, lack of focus and the physical environment are all barriers to effective communication.

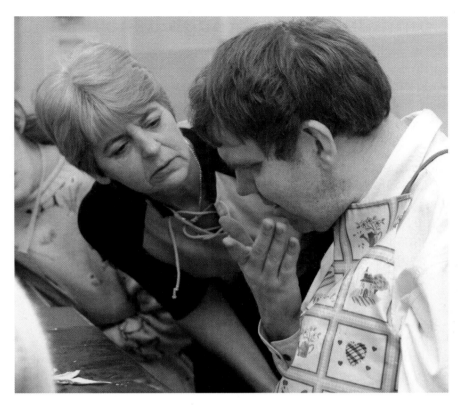

▲ People with learning disabilities may not have the words they need to express themselves.

Scenario: Why is Callum nervous?

One of Callum's support workers, Linda, speaks very loudly and quickly. Callum does not always understand what she is saying to him, and he feels uncomfortable because the tone of her voice makes him think that she is angry with him. Linda cannot understand why Callum appears so nervous when she is with him as she feels she is being friendly and doing everything she can to help him feel relaxed. After discussing the problem with her line manager, Linda starts to speak more slowly and quietly to Callum. As he becomes more relaxed and confident, their relationship improves.

Activity 4b

Personal barriers to communication

Think of a person with learning disabilities you work with regularly. List three personal barriers to communication they have and identify one way you could support them to overcome each barrier. Note down your ideas and discuss them with the person or someone who knows them well. See whether you can do one thing to make communication easier for that person in the next few days.

Communicating through behaviour

We all feel frustrated and hurt sometimes when we can't communicate what we want to say, or when we misunderstand what others have told us. Despite our frustration, we can do something when communication breaks down. We can repair the breakdown by saying, 'What do you mean by…?' and 'What I meant was…'

Many people with learning disabilities have had little opportunity to develop these skills. Where communication is less developed, as with people who have a severe or profound disability, they may have few opportunities to express their feelings and thoughts or to respond to what is happening to them. In situations like this, it's possible that challenging behaviour may develop as an alternative to more conventional ways of communicating.

Lack of understanding of any sort almost always makes people feel anxious. The world must feel like a very threatening and unpredictable place if things that cause you anxiety or fear occur every day.

Thinking point

Can you imagine what it must be like not being able to understand much of what is happening or being said by the people around you every day? How would this make you feel? What effect might it have on your emotional well-being? Would it make you happy or miserable?

▲ People with learning disabilities may have to resort to using behaviour to communicate.

Scenario: What does Bronwen like to eat?

Bronwen seems to understand everything that people say to her and usually agrees with whatever staff suggest when they discuss the food for the next few days. Carys has only just started working with Bronwen. After supporting her to make a list and do the shopping, she is really surprised when she pushes away the food they prepared screaming, 'No! No! No!'. When she talks this through with her line manager later, he explains that Bronwen always says 'yes' when support workers ask her something, because she wants to please them and that Carys should use other methods of finding out what she likes to eat, such as taking her to the fridge and asking her to point to her favourite foods.

Activity 4c

Communicating without words

In each of the situations below, an individual is communicating their wishes and needs without words.

Majid is on a course at his local college. The lecturer says, 'Do you remember that today we are visiting the local sports centre? Put your coat on, Majid, it's time to go.' When Majid remains seated and looks blankly at her, the lecturer says, 'Come on, Majid, we're all waiting for you. Hurry up!' Majid becomes distressed, bangs the table and refuses to move.

Neil is watching his favourite action film with the volume high. Ian, his support worker, is with him. Robert walks in from work. Neil looks at him and says, 'Hi, Rob. Have you had a good day?' Robert doesn't answer – he turns, walks out and goes to sit in his room.

Make notes on what feelings or wishes you think Majid and Robert are trying to communicate. Then think about similar situations in your workplace. In what ways do the people who you support convey their feelings and wishes without words?

Sometimes, when individuals can't get their message across through speech, they find other methods of conveying their feelings and frustrations, for example:

- taking things (instead of asking)
- pushing (instead of waiting or saying 'Excuse me')
- hitting (instead of saying 'Please don't do that')
- screaming (instead of asking 'Can we do something different now?').

When people behave like this they are often described as having challenging behaviours. It is usually easy to recognise challenging behaviours, but much more difficult to define them.

People with learning disabilities can challenge the support or service they are receiving by:

Key point
A person may sometimes act out their feelings through behaviour if those around them don't take the time to understand them.

Thinking point

Think about a time when someone you were talking to did not seem to understand the point you were trying to make, or when they did not seem to hear you properly. How did you feel? Did you show your feelings? If so, how?

- shouting and screaming
- being violent or aggressive
- being disruptive and interfering with other people
- wandering or running away
- self-injury, for example hitting or scratching themselves
- inappropriate intimate contact or sexual behaviour.

Behaviours are usually considered challenging because they meet one or more of the following criteria:

- they pose a risk of injury to the person or to other people
- they involve damage to property
- they make it difficult for staff or carers to work with and help the person
- they restrict the range of activities the person gets involved in.

To demonstrate that you have understood the information about communication, you should be able to discuss why it's important to know about factors affecting communication in relation to the people you support. The following example should help you do this.

Example 4: Factors that affect communication

Karli is a woman in her mid-thirties who is described as having severe learning disabilities. She doesn't communicate verbally, but with her own sign language. She lives in a residential home with three other women and attends college three days a week. The staff feel it's important for Karli to attend college to get her out of the house, learn new skills and meet other people.

Each morning, Karli has a lift to college from a support worker who then leaves. Karli is supported by a member of staff from the college who she likes. Each day, as soon as she arrives in the classroom, Karli indicates that she wants to go to the toilet. The toilet is quite a distance from the classroom and Karli walks slowly. A visit to the toilet can take around ten minutes and Karli indicates that she wants to go to the toilet three to four times during the morning. Typically, Karli engages in activities with the rest of the group for a few minutes and then pushes them away, or moves away, indicating that she is no longer interested in them. Occasionally, Karli appears to become frustrated and angry with other students or with the college worker who supports her. When this happens she hits out at them. This results in her being excluded from college for the rest of the week. When she returns, the cycle begins again.

1. Do you think Karli enjoys college? What evidence do you have to support your opinion?
2. If you think she isn't happy at college write down three ways you could find out some activities that she does enjoy.

Now turn to the commentary on this example on page 78.

Promoting effective communication

5

'I need support to speak up for myself. I want people to show that they have listened to me.'

Tracey, *Self-advocate*

Introduction

Communication is such a commonplace activity for most of us that we seldom give it a thought, although there are times when we have to choose our words carefully. But communication is about much more than just words. We also communicate non-verbally, and through the way that we listen to others. Communication is a vital element in developing the kind of relationship with a person with learning disabilities that will enable them to express their needs and wishes and you as a support worker to understand what it is they are trying to say. It will also help you to explain things in a way that the person will find easy to understand.

Learning outcomes

This chapter looks at:

- verbal communication
- non-verbal communication
- listening skills
- situations that need particularly sensitive communication
- aspects of communication and listening skills that vary between cultures
- issues surrounding the use of touch
- how to deal with not understanding or not being understood
- other methods of communication.

Types of communication

We communicate with each other in many ways. It is important that, as a support worker, you understand how communication takes place so that you can develop effective communication with the people you support.

Verbal communication

In the following picture there are no visual clues as to what the person may be saying. Sometimes we have to rely on the words someone uses.

▲ Sometimes we have to rely on the words someone uses because there are no visual clues.

Words and sentences

We can put words together in many different ways. The kind of words we use, the order we put them in and the length of the sentence all affect the clarity of the message. In general, the longer and more complex the sentence and the more difficult the words, the harder it is to understand. But we have other clues – volume and tone of voice.

Volume

Speaking loudly or softly can convey meaning. Shouting may indicate that people are arguing or some distance from each other or that a person has a hearing impairment. It may also indicate that people want to show support, such as cheering on a team at a football match, or praising a musician after a concert performance. Whispering could mean that the message was confidential or embarrassing or that the people talking were somewhere, such as a place of worship or a theatre, where it was important not to disturb others.

Tone

The voice can be changed to express different emotions or feelings, such as impatience, happiness, anger, pleasure, tenderness and so on. For instance, if you have to tell someone some bad news, your tone of voice would be serious. If you were talking about something amusing that had happened to you that day, your tone would be light.

Thinking point

Next time you watch the news on the television, or listen to the news on the radio, think about how the newsreaders change their tone of voice according to whether they are relaying a serious news item, or something more humorous.

Promoting effective communication

Effective verbal communication

In your work with people with learning disabilities you always need to keep in mind how you use verbal communication. It is helpful to match the words and sentences you use to the individual's ability, understanding and experience. For example, if a person you work with has difficulty using spoken language and uses mainly single words to communicate, it's a good idea to use only single words and short simple sentences when you speak to them. You can repeat the sentence to make sure the person understands. Take care not to say too much or ask too many questions at one time.

When working with people who have verbal skills, ask different kinds of questions, not just ones that require one-word answers or a gesture. For example, instead of asking, 'Where did you go at the weekend?' say, 'Tell me about your weekend'. If the person has difficulty answering such an open question, you can simplify it and do things in stages by asking, 'Did you go out?', 'Where did you go?', 'Tell me about it'. In time, the individual will become more skilled in answering more open questions.

Non-verbal communication

We communicate a great deal through non-verbal methods of communication – that is, through our facial expressions, body position, eye contact and gestures. As a support worker you will need to pay attention to body language, as it is a way of finding out more about the people you support, for example, how they are feeling and reacting to certain situations. You also need to be aware of your own non-verbal communication, as this will be important to the people you support and your colleagues.

Scenario: Understanding David

David is described as having severe learning disabilities. He is friendly and lively with a good sense of humour and loves to chat to people. He communicates verbally in short sentences. People who don't know David well sometimes find it hard to understand his speech. David prefers people to tell him if they don't understand what he is saying. He is very patient and will repeat it, adding large gestures and facial expressions until he gets his message across.

Activity 5a

Body language

◀ Body language can tell us a lot about how someone feels.

Look at the picture above and write a short sentence to describe what you think is happening. Now reread your sentence and note down how you reached that conclusion.

You can use the following clues to help you understand other people's non-verbal communication:

- the facial expression of both people
- the gestures they both are using
- the space between them
- eye contact
- their body positions.

Pay particular attention to people's faces, and especially their eyes, as this is a good way to understand how a person is feeling. Remember that sometimes our eyes communicate something different from our words.

Eye contact can be tricky, so you need to know the person well before you can be sure what they are telling you. Most people maintain eye contact if they want to communicate and are interested in what is happening or being discussed. Lack of eye contact can mean the person is unhappy or depressed or unwilling to communicate at that time. Remember that some people with autism find establishing and maintaining eye contact very difficult, so you will need to know the person well before you can truly understand their communication.

Body posture tells us a lot about how a person is feeling. People who are stooping or have their legs or arms crossed usually feel withdrawn or unhappy, whereas people who show an open body posture are usually more comfortable and calm. But there are cultural issues relating to body language and you need to understand the person's background and earlier experiences before you can really understand their body language.

If the person you support communicates mostly through body language and in other non-verbal ways, it is helpful when you are getting to know them to check your interpretation of their communication with their family and friends or others who know them well.

People who don't communicate verbally often benefit from other forms of communication. These include:

- sign language – a form of communication (e.g. British Sign Language) that uses hand signs combined with facial expression)
- sign system – a simplified sign language (e.g. Makaton) that has no grammar, designed specifically for a particular group of people
- symbol system – a method for people with limited or no speech that uses abstract symbols to represent objects or ideas and is designed for use in printed materials and on computers and other electronic devices (e.g. Blissymbols and Rebus)
- tactile system – a method that uses a series of raised dots to represent letters or groups of letters (e.g. Braille) or that uses raised symbols (e.g. Moon)
- photographs – a medium sometimes preferred by people with learning disabilities who find photographs more meaningful than symbols
- manual signing – a method of signing where letters are spelt out by positioning the fingers on the receiver's hand
- objects of reference – a method using different objects to represent choices, activities, people, feelings or daily routines.

Thinking point
Think about your own body language. How do you show with your body that you are relaxed, nervous or bored?

Key point
You should consider everything the person does as communication, including their words, facial expressions, gestures and body position.

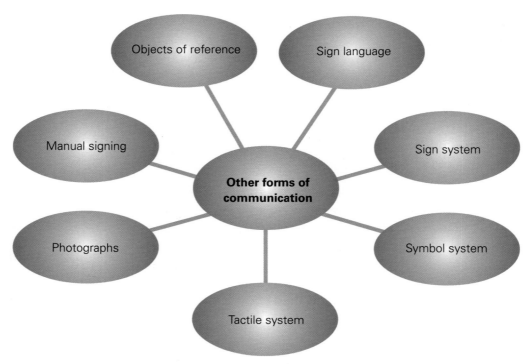

▲ People who don't communicate verbally often benefit from other forms of communication.

Find out about these other forms of communication from the person you support or their family, or seek advice from a colleague with experience.

Scenario: Communicating with Pat

Pat has a profound learning disability. She does not communicate verbally, and has a hearing impairment. Pat's support workers communicate with her using objects to represent the day's events. For example, to ask Pat if she would like a drink, her support worker will show her a mug. She will watch Pat's face carefully and if she smiles it means that she would.

Effective listening skills

Many people think listening is a natural and very easy skill, but most of us could benefit from improving our listening skills. It is all too easy to interrupt people or let our attention wander when others are talking. When you are supporting people who find communication hard, it is important that you respect their communication by listening carefully.

There are a number of things you can do to improve your listening skills:

- Give your full attention to the person who is speaking. Unless you know they don't like you to, look at them to make sure they know you are paying attention.
- Sit or stand facing the person. If your body is turned away from them, they may think you aren't listening.
- Concentrate on what they are saying.
- Don't interrupt – let them finish speaking before you start.
- Listen for the main points the person is trying to get across and repeat them back to them to check you fully understand what is being said.
- If you don't understand what they are saying – ask!
- Give feedback – nod, smile or say something like 'mm,' or 'uh-huh'.

Scenario: Going to the cinema with Shaun

Phil supports Shaun on a visit to the cinema. After the film, Shaun becomes quiet and withdrawn, unlike his usual self. Phil thinks that Shaun may have been upset by something in the film. Instead of trying to talk to Shaun in the noise and bustle of the house where he lives, Phil suggests that they call in at a café on the way home. In a quiet seating area, where he can give Shaun his full attention, Phil asks Shaun what he thought about the film.

Communication in a sensitive situation

In your day-to-day work supporting people you will sometimes be involved in sensitive situations, such as when you go with someone to the doctor or support someone who is upset, or when you provide intimate personal care or talk to someone about confidential matters.

In these situations you will need to ensure that the person you are supporting is at the centre of what you are doing and that you do everything you can to understand and promote their needs and wishes. How you handle a sensitive situation can have a long-term effect on how the person feels and reacts and on their relationship with you, so you should pay particular attention to your communication when working in sensitive situations. The following table gives some examples of good practice in such situations.

Key point
In sensitive situations you should think carefully about your communication. Put the person at the centre, take your time, think about where you communicate and adjust your communication to suit their needs.

Working in a sensitive situation	
Good practice idea	**Reason for working in this way**
Listen carefully to what the person is telling you and reflect back what the person has told you.	It shows respect. Reflecting back the key points of the conversation can reassure the person you have correctly understood what they are telling you.
Think about where you talk to the person. It may be best to look for a quiet place where you will not be overheard.	Confidentiality and privacy are important. The person may feel more confident about talking to you if you are not being overheard.
Take your time and communicate in a way that is most suitable for the person. Adjust the words you use, your tone, the length of your sentences and the use of signs or symbols so that they are appropriate for the person and the matter you are discussing. Watch carefully for the person's responses, in both their verbal and non-verbal communication.	It shows you are working in a person-centred way and respecting the person's needs. Reflecting their vocabulary, pace and signs shows their communication pattern is acceptable.
If possible, check with the person some while later to see whether they have understood everything or have thought of more points they want to discuss.	This gives an opportunity to check the understanding of the person involved as well as your own understanding. It also gives an opportunity to raise any other issues following a time for **reflection**.

reflection
careful consideration of ideas and issues

Cultural differences and communication

Someone's culture is not simply about the language they use or the way they dress. It's much more than that – it defines what people believe and the way they think, feel and behave. It is important to be aware that aspects of communication differ between cultures and that differences in communication can sometimes create barriers. You should think about how these can be overcome.

Language differences

The person you support and their family may speak a different language from you, or they may speak one language at home and a different one when they're attending a day service or other activity. Some people find it easy to switch between languages, but others find it difficult.

For example, some people who communicate in more than one language:

- may be more skilled in one than the other and therefore appear to understand, but miss important information
- might cope in familiar settings but have difficulty in unfamiliar situations

- may understand what you are saying but their family members may not
- may find your accent difficult to understand.

Sometimes it isn't possible to translate literally from one language into another. This may be because there are no equivalent words or because the concept itself may play an unimportant part in the culture or be contradictory to the values of the culture.

There may be other language barriers:

- Information may not be available in the necessary language so that it is difficult for people to find out about services available to them.
- Some languages don't have written scripts. For example, Mirpuri is a spoken but not written dialect of Punjabi.
- Some translated information is highly specialised and not accessible to many people, including people with a learning disability.
- Some words, such as 'love' and 'duck', are acceptable in some parts of the UK but offensive in others.

Scenario: Marko's two languages

Marko and his family came to England from Croatia when he was 15. His first language is Serbo-Croat, although he has learned some English in the last ten years. All his family speak Serbo-Croat at home, although his sisters also speak excellent English. When Marko was doing his person-centred plan it was really important that the meetings were in both English and Serbo-Croat, as Marko finds it easier to talk about his dreams and hopes for the future in his first language.

Conceptual and ethical differences

Cultural differences may occur because of geographical or organisational variations.

Different cultures have different concepts of disability, which may lead to a lack of information or a conflict of opinion about some disabilities. For example, autism as it is known in most of Europe and North America is not recognised by some other cultures, which have their own equally valid understanding of the same characteristics.

The service a person attends may have a different ethos and atmosphere to the one they experience at home. Although the service may have information about the person's religion and culture they may not have appropriate knowledge and expertise to deliver the required services. For example, a person from an orthodox Jewish background would have special requirements for prayers, food and cleanliness.

Non-verbal communication differences

It's not only verbal communication where there can be cultural differences. Non-verbal cues vary between cultures and can lead to misinterpretation. For example, among some Hindu communities, folding one's arms is a sign of humility. In a western culture this could be a sign of stubbornness or aggression.

Eye contact is an important means of non-verbal communication in many cultures, and lack of eye contact is seen as a barrier to communication in some western cultures. However, Somali children are taught not to make eye contact with adults. This could clearly have implications for those working with children from a Somali family.

Images and symbols can have different meanings in different cultures so you need to think about the different interpretation of images that you use. In most western cultures, a 'thumbs-up' symbol is commonly used to represent a positive gesture in documents or posters, but in many Arabic cultures this can be seen as negative and insulting.

Using touch to communicate

Physical contact may be used as a means of communication with people with a learning disability, but it can be used both appropriately and inappropriately.

Appropriate physical contact

Touch can be particularly useful in communicating, such as in the following situations.

- **When someone has a hearing impairment.** Catherine has a hearing impairment in addition to her learning disability. She is watching television. Mary approaches her and touches her lightly on the arm, saying, 'Tea's ready, Catherine – come and sit at the table.'
- **When someone needs help with direction.** Erica is at the swimming baths with Julie. 'This cubicle's empty. You can change in here,' she says, and takes Julie by the arm to guide her into the cubicle.
- **When someone is congratulated.** Yaqoob shows Luke the certificate of achievement presented to him at college that day. Luke shakes his hand and says, 'Well done, mate – I knew you could do it!'

In your own work you may find physical contact a useful way of communicating with people with learning disabilities or of encouraging them to communicate with you, such as:

- putting your hand on someone's shoulder as you say 'Hello'
- tapping someone lightly to draw their attention
- catching hold of someone's arm to ask them to wait
- putting your arm round someone's shoulder to encourage them.

Inappropriate physical contact

There are times when physical contact is a helpful and appropriate part of communicating. There are other times when it definitely isn't, such as in the following situations.

- **When the action is disrespectful or patronising.** Sarah has a habit of patting people on the head or on the knee as she says 'Good morning' to the people with learning disabilities at the day service where she works. Although some people respond and seem to enjoy it, others get annoyed. Even if some people with learning disabilities respond, this kind of action in the workplace is seldom appropriate. Not only is it intrusive, it's also an undignified way of treating adults. It's unlikely that Sarah would behave like this with her non-disabled friends or colleagues, so she should have the same respect for people with learning disabilities. It's also obvious that some of them don't want Sarah to do this, so she's being disrespectful to the people involved.
- **When physical contact is overused.** Alan runs the football team. He often puts his arms around the shoulders of the people with learning disabilities who are in the team, teasing them, joking with them and pushing them away if they tease him. This is a more difficult situation to give an opinion about. In some situations, these kinds of actions could be appropriate, help to improve communication and strengthen relationships. It depends where it happens and how often. It also depends on how different people respond and whether they are comfortable with it.

As well as the examples of inappropriate physical contact described above, there are other situations when communication through inappropriate physical contact is much more serious:

- **When physical contact causes pain.** For example, when a grip or a touch is too forceful.
- **When there is a sexual element involved.** For example, when someone supporting an individual with a learning disability takes advantage of the fact that the individual likes them and uses physical contact to tease the person or to encourage a state of excitement or sexual arousal.

When physical contact involves unnecessary touching of intimate parts of the body. This should never happen as part of ordinary communication, even in fun. It can be tricky when the person with learning disabilities has physical disabilities and is highly dependent, but there should be guidelines and support for staff in dealing with these situations.

When there are cultural differences in relation to physical contact. In some cultures, any physical contact between members of the opposite sex is inappropriate. Some cultures consider particular parts of the body to be sacred or particularly dignified, for example, the head. Any physical contact with these areas can be disrespectful.

Key point

Physical contact is inappropriate when it is intrusive or disrespectful, or when the person does not want physical contact. Communication through physical contact is always inappropriate if it involves pain, sexual intent or unnecessary touching of intimate parts of the body.

Feelings about physical contact

One of the best ways to decide whether or not physical contact is appropriate is to be guided by the person and by the policy of your organisation. We all differ in the kind of physical contact we feel comfortable with. Often this depends on the experiences we've had and on our environment. Sometimes it depends on what's expected in the person's culture.

Thinking point

Think about your own responses to touch. Are there people who regularly use touch to communicate with you in your daily life? What form does this touch take and how do you feel about it? Are there some people who you definitely don't want to touch you? If so, why is this and how do you let them know how you feel?

You'll sometimes be in ▶ situations where you use physical contact to help with communication.

As a support worker, you'll often be in situations where you use physical contact quite naturally to help with communication. Sometimes, however, someone you are working with may overreact, or react differently from what you expect. Sometimes they may show you quite clearly that they aren't happy or comfortable with what you're doing, perhaps with a shrug or by pushing you away or by saying quite plainly, 'Don't do that.'

You should find out the range and extent of physical contact an individual is comfortable with. There are a number of ways you can do this in your own work situation:

- **Be sensitive to both verbal and non-verbal feedback.** Sometimes it is impossible not to notice this as some people react strongly by shouting or screaming when anyone touches them. At other times, a quiet voice saying, 'Don't' can be easily overlooked.
- **Question people when they react to physical contact.** This can be done quite simply and naturally without much fuss – 'Sorry, Paulo. Is something wrong?', 'I don't think you like that Martha. Right?' It can also be done in discussion groups where individuals talk about what kinds of touch they do and don't like. This can be related to incidents that have happened recently.
- **Use drama to explore people's feelings about physical contact in a non-threatening way.** This can often lead to a discussion about what people do and don't like and the reasons why.
- **Be observant as you go about your daily work, taking notice of non-verbal behaviours or feedback.** For example, when individuals react to being touched by pushing the person away, turning away, moving out of range or shrugging the person off.

Activity 5b

Physical contact

Think about an individual with learning disabilities who you support. How do you know whether they find physical contact an acceptable way of communication? Do they accept touch from some people rather than others? Why do you think this is? If possible ask them, to check whether you were right.

Dealing with misunderstanding

You may find that when you are supporting a person there are occasions when you won't fully understand what they are trying to communicate to you. Remember, if you don't understand what a person is trying to communicate to you, it isn't their fault. When you ask them to repeat their communication, apologise for not understanding and never blame them for not communicating clearly. You could say something like, 'I'm sorry, I'm having difficulty understanding what you said. Can you help me by speaking more slowly?' You could also ask a colleague or family carer, who might know the person better, to help you understand. You could also use pictures or signs – the person may be able to point or sign more easily than speaking. Take your time and be creative. Give the person time to express themselves in other ways.

If the person you are supporting doesn't understand you then you could:

- repeat what you've said using shorter sentences and fewer words
- communicate more slowly and allow the person more time to understand
- support what you're saying with signs or pictures as appropriate
- think about whether the environment is too noisy or distracting
- speak more clearly, especially if your native language or accent is unfamiliar to the person
- think more about your non-verbal communication and whether your body language is saying something different from your words and confusing the person.

Other methods of communication

There are a number of other aids you can use to help a person with a learning disability communicate.

Sign language

Some people with learning disabilities communicate in a sign language called Makaton, which is based on British Sign Language. You may have the opportunity to learn this in your new role.

Objects of reference

These are objects that are chosen to represent activities, people, feelings or ideas. They can be helpful in communicating with someone who doesn't respond to other forms of communication.

Pictures and symbols

These can be used in a number of ways. They can be added to written information to make this more accessible or understandable for people with learning disabilities. They can also be used with individuals to help them make choices, or to understand events that will happen that day. There is a variety of symbols, communication systems and picture banks that have been specially developed for use with people with learning disabilities. If these are used in the organisation you work for you will be given training in how to use them properly.

To demonstrate that you have understood the information about promoting effective communication, you should be able to discuss ways in which you can communicate effectively with the people you support. The following example should help you do this.

Example 5: Communicating effectively

Benjamin is a young man in his twenties with a real passion for cooking. He is described as having a learning disability. He doesn't communicate very well verbally, but he appears to understand when people talk to him. He has attended a catering course run by a local charity and they have found him a work placement in a local café. His support worker, Wen, accompanies him there on the bus, stays for a short while to check everything is OK and later returns to accompany him home. The placement has run smoothly for two months, but one day the café manager telephones Wen to ask him to go home early with Benjamin. He says that during his break Benjamin sat next to one of the waitresses and put his hand on her leg. The waitress became very upset. The manager says Benjamin must stay at home for the rest of the week so that he can decide whether Benjamin ought to continue the placement.

1. Make a list of the areas Wen will need to discuss with Benjamin.
2. What additional communication methods could he use?
3. How can Wen ensure he deals sensitively with this situation?

Now turn to the commentary on this example on page 79.

6

Keeping written records

'Keeping good records is important so that we can support people well. When you keep good records you must keep to the facts and only record the important details.'

Terry Goodwin, *Support worker*

Introduction

As well as verbal communication and the use of body language to exchange information, written records and reports are essential to all types of social care support. The type and extent of record keeping required will depend on the kind of work you do and the way your service is run. If you work for a large organisation it is likely that you will be required to keep more records than if you are employed by an individual receiving direct payments or individual budgets. Certain records are mandatory for some types of service. This means that you are required by law to keep them. Some records relate only to the organisation or individual you work for. Whether you work for an organisation or an individual, you will be required to complete some written records as part of your work.

Learning outcomes

This chapter covers:

- the importance of record keeping when supporting a person with a learning disability
- the purpose of record keeping
- good practice in record keeping
- how support workers can contribute to records and reports
- the main points of the Data Protection Act 1998 and other legislation.

The importance of records and reports

In the not too distant past, records and reports were considered to be the property of 'professionals'. A vast amount of information was kept about people with learning disabilities and individuals were not expected to read or have access to the information that was held about them. They were not expected to attend meetings where personal information about them was discussed and plans for their future were made. Nowadays, things are changing.

Most services that support people with learning disabilities aim to give individuals more independence and control over their own lives. Many people with learning disabilities are supported to develop their own person-centred plans. Now it is commonplace for individuals to take an active part in meetings held about them or to chair the meeting. Many people hold information and records about themselves or have access to records held about them.

It is important, as you read this chapter about record keeping, and relate it to your own practice, that you bear in mind that the people you support should be as fully involved as possible in the record-keeping process. This can mean making records easier to read and understand, involving people with learning disabilities in report writing and record keeping where possible, and checking that they are aware of the information held about them and why it is held.

Records and reports serve many purposes. They:

- provide us with important and relevant background information about a person's life before we knew them
- help us keep track of events over a period of time
- help us to pass on relevant information to other people
- help to bridge gaps between one person's knowledge and another person's knowledge
- can show progress and development
- show how well a service is doing its job.

How involved you get in them will depend on the type of work you do and the way your service is run.

You may be surprised at the amount of record keeping that your job involves. However, records and reports are essential aspects of all services. Keeping effective records and reports is key to ensuring that an individual with learning disabilities is supported properly. Making records accessible to the people they are about is an important new challenge for social care workers and organisations.

Thinking point
How would you feel if your friends and colleagues had access to very private and personal information about your life?

▲ Records and reports help us keep track of events over a period of time.

One organisation that supports people with learning disabilities keeps the following written records:

- initial assessments and history
- day books/contact sheets
- medical records
- accident records
- personal finance records
- bank account details
- individual plans
- support plans
- person-centred plans
- review reports
- behavioural management strategies
- monitoring forms.

The organisation also keeps other records, such as risk assessments, safety records, fire drills, fridge and freezer temperatures, staff reviews and appraisals and financial records. Some of these records relate to staff and some to the safety and protection of both staff and individuals with learning disabilities. All the records are important in a high-quality service.

Activity 6a
Keeping records

Look at the list of records above and note down those which are also kept by your organisation and any other records not already listed that you are required to keep.

Does the person you support have access to the records you have listed? Are they in a format they can understand? If there are records the person does not have access to, talk to your line manager to find out why.

Key point
Keeping effective records and reports is key to ensuring that a person is supported properly.

Types of record
Record of support
The majority of services will require their workers to record the support they have given to an individual on a daily basis. This information can take the form of a diary, a log book or a contact sheet.

The following is an example of part of a diary entry for one individual with a learning disability.

Friday 10 November

Andrew got up, showered and dressed following his support plan. He had breakfast and watched television in his room for half an hour. At 10.30 he went swimming at Farm Road swimming baths supported by Alan and Carol. He stayed in the water for 30 minutes. He enjoyed the visit, laughing and splashing Carol. When he was dressed he had a cup of coffee and a cake in the coffee bar at the swimming baths and returned home at 12.30.

▲ You may need to keep a diary or log book for the person you support.

A record of support is important because it:

- records the support that took place, the time and the support worker
- means that the quality of the support given to an individual can be checked by the organisation and by external bodies and inspectors
- records events so that it can be used at a later date by a support worker to remind the person with learning disabilities what has happened.

Incident report

You may be required to record a particular event, such as an accident, or a situation that occurred unexpectedly, such as an incidence of challenging behaviour. You will need to record the date, time and location of the incident as well as everyone who was involved and any witnesses. This type of record is important because:

- serious incidents need to be reported to your manager and to the service's inspector so that they can be properly investigated
- it may be used to monitor an individual's support and care, as well as their behaviour
- patterns of behaviour and what caused them can be identified and appropriate action taken to prevent them from happening in the future.

Here is an example of an incident report.

INCIDENT REPORT

Date 26.2.07   **Time of incident** 8.30am

Staff involved in the incident

First name	Surname	Signature	Male/female	Post
Alicia	Macdonald		F	Support worker
Terry	Griffiths		M	Support worker

Tenant involved in the incident

First name	Surname	Signature	Male/female	Address
Judith	Howard		F	24 Kings Croft Newacre

Description of the incident

At 8.30am Terry arrived to accompany Judith to college. Judith was still eating her breakfast very slowly and ignored Terry. I asked her to hurry up as she would be late for college. Judith tipped her cereal bowl over the table and threw her mug of tea at the wall. She said, 'I hate college and I'm never going again.' She got up and ran to her room crying. I left her alone for 10 minutes then I went up to her room to see her. She had stopped crying and was sitting quietly. I asked her again whether she wanted to go to college and she said, 'I don't want to go to college today'. She apologised for shouting earlier. I said she did not have to go if she did not want to and asked her to come downstairs and help me to clean up the cereal and the tea. She did this and by 9.30am she was sitting in the lounge reading a magazine.

Report completed by: A. MACDONALD   **Signature** A. Macdonald   **Time** 10.30

Senior staff on duty: L. MOORE   **Signature** L. Moore   **Date** 27.2.07

▲ You may need to complete an incident report form for the person you support.

The purpose of record keeping

The amount of recording that staff are expected to do varies from organisation to organisation. If you look back to the types of records you listed in Activity 6a (see page 56), you will see that these refer to particular occasions or activities, for example when:

- staff hand over to other colleagues after their shift
- a support worker has visited or met with a person they are supporting
- there is an accident
- there is an incident that requires recording or further action
- there is a review meeting with a particular person with learning disabilities
- medication or medical conditions have implications for work with a particular person with learning disabilities
- services plan activities with a person
- progress is assessed and new individual plans developed
- people show behaviour that challenges the service
- a friend or relative has communicated with the service
- an action plan is developed as a result of the person-centred planning process.

Good practice in record keeping

Your role in using and contributing to records and reports

The *Code of Practice for Social Care Workers* clearly states the responsibilities of all social care workers regarding recording information clearly and accurately, as required by the organisation they work for:

> 'As a social care worker you must be accountable for the quality of your work… this includes… maintaining clear and accurate records as required by procedures established for your work'

You must keep this in mind in all record keeping that you undertake.

Selecting and gathering information for recording purposes

Different kinds of forms require different kinds of information. Sometimes it isn't easy to decide what to write and how much to include:

- Sometimes factual information is required, for example, when did Rod visit Leroy?

Policy reference
Code of Practice for Social Care Workers
2002 General Social Care Council 2002

- Sometimes you have to make a judgement about a situation and then check this out, for example, was Rashid upset because he could not go to visit his sister or was there another reason?
- Sometimes you have to select and summarise information from another source, such as taking information from Sandra's person-centred plan in order to plan new activities with her.

Here are some ideas for selecting and gathering information:

- Develop good observation skills to help you to gather facts and assess a situation. Effective observation means not jumping to conclusions, but writing down what you actually see or hear. For example, instead of writing, 'Alec was upset this morning', you could write, 'Alec shouted out loudly when Jason sat down beside him at break time and cried until lunch time'. This gives much more of an idea of what you actually observed and also gives you some idea of what the reason might be for Alec's behaviour. You can also observe the behaviour of someone who can't communicate verbally to interpret how they felt about a situation. For example, 'Alison put her fingers in her ears when Martin and Stella were arguing'.
- Ask the person with learning disabilities to tell you what they saw or heard to add to what you observed.
- Discuss events with other colleagues to check out whether their observations are similar to yours. If they aren't, try to reach agreement, involving a third person if necessary.
- Ask yourself whether the information you select is needed for this particular purpose, or whether it is irrelevant. For example, Anstey's reports for review meetings are always far too long so nobody ever reads them. He includes events far back in the past, and detailed analysis of practically everything the individual has done and said since the last meeting. He needs to learn to select relevant information and to summarise it. On the other hand, Sue's reports are so short and subjective, with so few facts, that they tell you nothing.
- Use other well-written reports and records as examples. This means reports that:
  - are short and to the point
  - give facts rather than your own opinions or vague phrases such as 'seems happy and well adjusted'
  - include the kind of information you need to get on with your work
  - are written in a way that you would want information written about yourself.

Key point
Keeping clear and accurate records is an important part of your role as a social care worker.

Accuracy of information

The information you record should be relevant, clear, concise and factually accurate. Look at the following examples of information that has been written in reports.

What was written	What should have been written
Sinead didn't want to wash this morning and was a real pain.	Sinead refused to have a wash this morning.
Imran seemed to enjoy his morning at the day service.	While he was at the day service Imran smiled and laughed. He took part in all the activities.

Activity 6b

Accuracy of records

Rewrite the following examples so that they are clear, concise and factually accurate.

- John's behaviour in the café was disgusting.
- Conor was late for college again. I think the staff are getting fed up with him. He played cards at lunch time, which was good because it stopped him annoying the other students.
- Becky loved the trip to the park. She walked for miles and was brilliant in the pub afterwards.

Discuss with your manager or an experienced colleague whether they agree with your changes.

Records and anti-discriminatory language

In the examples above you probably noticed some examples of negative language, for example, 'pain' and 'disgusting'. These words express negative judgements and might be seen as evidence of verbal abuse or discrimination on the basis of an individual's learning disability. Any negative judgements that are made in reports should be based on evidence and not the personal opinion of the writer. All language used in reports should be anti-discriminatory. When writing any report, read it through and think about how you would feel if it was written about you. If you are unhappy with the language used or the content it is more than likely that the person you are writing about would be as well.

Thinking point

Have you ever had anything written about you that you did not agree with? How did you feel? What, if anything, did you do about it?

Signing and dating records and reports

It is important to sign records and reports because signatures:

- tell you who to go to if you need more information
- can help when organising activities, showing which staff work best with which person with learning disabilities and who has had fewer opportunities to work with whom
- indicate that you are doing a professional job.

It is important to date records and reports because dates:

- enable you to see whether something is still relevant today or is outdated
- tell you how long something has been going on
- help you to put things in sequence and follow progress
- tell you whether records are up to date or have been neglected.

The Data Protection Act and other legislation

Policy reference
Principles of the Data Protection Act 1998

Data Protection Act 1998
www.opci.gov.uk

The Data Protection Act 1998 gives individuals certain rights about any information that is held about them and places obligations on those who hold and process the information. The Act applies to information held about you as a worker as well as the information about the people you support. There are eight principles of good practice that must be adhered to when handling information.

Data must be:

- fairly and lawfully processed
- processed for limited purposes and not used for any other purpose other than the one for which it was obtained
- adequate, relevant and not excessive
- accurate and up to date
- kept no longer than necessary
- processed in accordance with the individual's rights
- secure
- transferred to countries outside the European Economic Area only if that country has adequate protection for the individual.

The Caldicott Principles

Policy reference
The Caldicott Principles

Caldicott Report (1997)
Department of Health

The Caldicott Report (1997) set out six general principles that the NHS Executive believes health and social care organisations should use when reviewing information held about the people who use its services. They are used to describe the confidentiality and security of information held by social care and health services and partners regarding the people they support.

The following principles of good practice should be observed:

- A formal justification of purpose is required prior to sharing any information with others.
- Identifiable information (about a particular person) is to be transferred only when absolutely necessary.
- Information should be limited to the minimum required only.
- Access to information should be on a need-to-know basis only.
- All staff must understand their responsibilities in sharing information.
- All staff should comply with and understand the law.

You will see that the Caldicott Principles link closely to the principles of the Data Protection Act, and together they give clear guidance about storing information within an organisation. During your induction you should be told about the data protection policies and procedures for your organisation or the person you support.

Storing information

Systems for storing all personal information – for example names, addresses, telephone numbers, employment details, bank details, and so on – must be operated under the terms of the Data Protection Act. Organisations should have clear policies that show how they comply with the Act.

▲ Some information is probably held on a computer within your service.

You will probably find that the following information is held on computer within your service:

- databases of information about people and organisations
- people's names and addresses
- individual assessments
- records and reports of review procedures
- medical records
- financial accounts.

Scenario: Sahida's induction

Sahida works for Lowshire Social Care and Health Department. At her induction she is given information about the Intranet for Lowshire employees. The Intranet can only be accessed by a password and there are different levels of access for different types of employee. Sahida is able to access all policies and procedures, as well as records relating to the individuals she supports.

In addition, at least some of the following information may also be kept within your organisation:

- card indexes with factual information like names and addresses
- filing cabinet systems where information is stored alphabetically or under different categories
- record systems with information on individual programmes and achievements
- medical records
- personal financial records.

Most services have a formal policy on access to records. However, in practice the policy is often overlooked and staff develop shortcuts to make it easier to get the information they need. This in turn can increase the chances of confidential information getting into the wrong hands.

For example, many of the records you will be dealing with will contain information that is personal and private. It's therefore essential to treat these records in a confidential way. This means that you only use the information in ways required by your employer – that is, in ways that are directly related to your job. You must not pass on the information about an individual to anyone other than those who need it to do their job. Don't forget that confidentiality includes what you say to your family and friends at home or in the pub.

Passing on information verbally

There will be many occasions when you need to talk to a colleague about someone you support. This could be to pass on important information, ask advice or raise concerns. You should take care to ensure that these conversations are conducted away from anyone who does not need to be involved, including colleagues and others who use the services.

The passing on of information that other people need to know to do their job properly is very different from casually discussing the private life of someone you support with a colleague. You would be very unusual if you could honestly answer that you had never done this.

A person with learning disabilities will have the same feelings about hearing their private life discussed that you would have, but may not be able to express them verbally. Remember not to gossip about the people you support. You may also need to explain confidentiality to the people with learning disabilities you work with if they too are gossiping about private matters and other people's lives. Confidentiality is important to all of us.

To demonstrate that you understand the information about good record keeping you should be able to discuss the importance of record keeping and examples of good practice in relation to the people you support. The following example should help you do this.

Thinking point
How would you feel if you overheard your colleagues discussing your private life?

Example 6: Record keeping

Staff at an organisation who support people to live independently have developed records that are accessible to the people they support. Some use pictures and symbols that the person finds easier to understand. Record keeping is kept to a minimum. A support plan is drawn up with each person. The person is asked whether a file can be kept in their home to record the times and dates of visits, support provided, and other records, such as if a person is supported to take their medication. After each visit the support worker completes a daily record of support which is explained to the individual, who then signs it. All the people supported by the organisation are also aware of the other records that are kept about them in the main office. They have been informed that they can see them at any time or have them explained if necessary.

1. Identify three areas of good practice in the example above.
2. Are similar procedures in place where you work? If not, could the current procedures be improved?
3. Discuss this example with your line manager to find out more about record keeping in your organisation.

Now turn to the commentary on this example on page 79.

7

Your personal development as a learning disability worker

'Some people want to progress in their work, some want to stay as they are. It's about personal preference, but in the end the people who benefit are the people we support.'

Eileen, *Support worker*

Introduction

The people with learning disabilities you support and their families have a right to expect high-quality care from you and the service you work for. You have a responsibility to always provide the best possible support that you can and the organisation you work for has a responsibility to provide you with the learning opportunities you need to carry out your job to a high standard. Induction training is just the start of your development as a learning disability worker and it is the beginning of a journey of learning, qualifications and reflection.

Learning outcomes

This chapter looks at:

- why it is important for support workers to gain knowledge and skills and develop themselves in their work
- types of learning and development used by the service
- the need to be a reflective worker
- the purpose of supervision
- ways to make supervision effective
- how to write your personal development plan.

Gaining new knowledge and skills

The quality of the service an organisation provides is very closely linked with the quality of the staff it employs. Good organisations understand that the personal development of all of its workers is key to the provision of a quality service to people with learning disabilities. While your organisation will have put in place systems such as those described below to enable its staff to develop knowledge and skills, it's also up to you to take responsibility for your own learning. The *Code of Practice* for England says that as a social care worker you must 'undertake relevant training to maintain your knowledge and skills'.

When you begin your job working with people with learning disabilities you will have induction training. The length of the training and how it is delivered will vary between organisations. However, this should be just the start of your personal development as a learning disability worker. You will probably have been employed because of the knowledge and skills you already have, but your employer may also have seen the potential you have as an individual to gain new skills and knowledge and develop both in your present role and in future roles within the organisation. It is your responsibility to make the most of the opportunities that are presented to gain new skills and knowledge.

Scenario: Paulet's training

On the first day of her induction course as a new support worker, Paulet felt very nervous. She had not been in a classroom for many years and did not feel confident about talking in a group or doing written work. Each day after her course Paulet began to feel increasingly interested in and excited by what she was learning. It became easier to complete the written work, and Paulet found that her colleagues valued what she had to say in the training sessions. After her induction, Paulet put herself forward for other training courses and she is now completing her first qualification.

Types of learning and development

During your induction as a new worker you are likely to be given information about how the organisation trains and develops its staff. There may be a training officer who is responsible for all training in the organisation, and the organisation may employ trainers who will deliver some or all of the training. The service might employ outside organisations with specialist expertise to deliver some of the training, for example first aid, food hygiene or lifting and handling.

However, gaining knowledge and learning new skills isn't just about attending as many training courses and taking as many qualifications as you can. There are many informal ways in which this can happen. The people you support, your colleagues and family carers are often excellent sources of information for new workers and you should always be open to asking others if there is something you are unsure about.

Here are some examples of how one support worker gained new knowledge and skills during one week in his new role.

Key point
Gaining new knowledge and skills can take place formally in training sessions and informally as you learn from people with learning disabilities, their relatives, your colleagues and managers.

Learning and development	
Situation/activity	**What I learned**
Supporting Ben to go to the pub	Talked to him about the visit first. Read the notes in his support plan. Discussed with my line manager what I should do. Last Wednesday went with Phil and Ben and asked lots of questions. This week went on my own with Ben.
Lifting and handling – attended training last Thursday	Went on course. Discussed with my line manager how I should use what I learnt on the course when lifting Ben in and out of his wheelchair. Watched Phil as he lifted Ben to be sure I got everything right.
Finding out about Ben's passion for Stoke City Football Club	Spoke to Ben and his dad about the club and how long they had been fans. Spoke to Ben's dad about what they currently do on match days – where they park, where they sit, etc. Looked at some of Ben's old match programmes and his DVDs with him.

Activity 7a

Learning and development

Think about the work you have done within your organisation in the last month. Note down some of the things you have learned and the situations you learned them in and discuss them with your line manager in your next supervision session.

The need to be a reflective worker

In everyday life we are always learning from experience. When something goes really well we can use our knowledge of what we did right in similar situations. Similarly, when something has gone disastrously wrong we can look back and think, 'If only I'd done such and such differently'. This is just the same in your role as a learning disability worker. By developing the habit of regularly reflecting on what you do day to day, you can improve how you support people.

Reflecting on a situation can be seen as a four-stage process:

- **Stage 1.** Something different or out of the ordinary happens in your day-to-day support of a person with a learning disability.

Thinking point

When you have had a good day at work do you reflect on what went well? Similarly, if you have had a bad day do you think about what went wrong and what you could have done to change it?

- **Stage 2.** Think through the event or situation to better understand what has happened. Look at what happened from the perspective of the different people involved. Think about the possible reasons for a person's behaviour and the effect of the environment or the other people involved.
- **Stage 3.** Reflect on a specific action or event in the light of your wider knowledge and understanding. Use any training or coaching from a more experienced colleague to help you make sense of the event.
- **Stage 4.** Use the ideas from your reflection to change your day-to-day practice.

This four-stage process is based on a well-known theory of learning called Kolb's cycle of experiential learning.

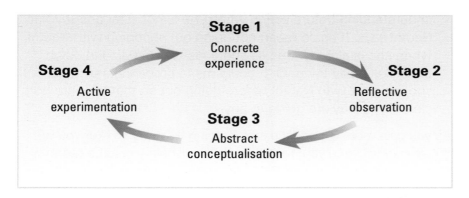

▲ Kolb's learning cycle

Activity 7b

Reflection

Reflect on the following situation using the four-stage process and make notes of what you learn.

Amy has been supporting Naomi for nearly two months and has gradually learnt how she prefers to communicate with her personal assistants. Mostly, Amy uses single words and a lot of facial expression to let people know how she feels and what she wants to do. When they are doing Amy's weekly shop at the supermarket Naomi thinks that Amy said she wanted muffins and walks with her to the cake aisle. Naomi actually said she wanted Marmite and when they got to the muffins she began to shout and push Amy and got quite upset. Amy was really surprised by her reaction and at first couldn't think why Naomi had reacted so negatively and strongly.

You may have written something like the following:

- **Stage 1. Something out of the ordinary happens.** Naomi reacted so negatively to Amy in the supermarket because she confused her request for Marmite with muffins.
- **Stage 2. Think through the event.** For Amy this might involve thinking through the situation again from Naomi's perspective and comparing it to other times they have gone to the supermarket and other times she has misunderstood what Naomi said.
- **Stage 3. Reflect on the event in the light of your wider knowledge and understanding.** For Amy this could mean thinking about Naomi's communication and reaction in the light of her recent training on communication and managing behaviour and looking at her notes from the training day she went to.
- **Stage 4. Use the ideas from your reflection to change your day-to-day practice.** For Amy this could mean checking her understanding before acting when she is not clear about what Naomi says. It could mean not going out shopping with Naomi when she is already tired as she finds walking up and down the aisles really tiring. Or it could mean preparing a pictorial shopping list with Naomi before going out so that they are both clear what they are going to buy.

As you gain more experience as a learning disability worker you will find that developing your reflective skills will help you to be more responsive to the needs of the people you support and more person centred in your day-to-day work. As well as developing your own skills as a reflective worker you will also find it very powerful to reflect with colleagues on the support you all provide. You can do this through team meetings or with your line manager in supervision.

Supervision in the workplace

One of the most important aspects of your development as a learning disability worker is having time to reflect on what you are doing and learning from it. Sharing this experience with someone else can help give you insights into your own abilities, strengths and needs.

Supervision is normally carried out by your immediate line manager but in some circumstances may be carried out by someone else. If you are a personal assistant employed directly by a person with a learning disability your supervision may be carried out by them or possibly by someone else who organises their personal assistants for them. The way supervision is done varies from workplace to workplace, but it is something which should be happening regularly in every service.

Key point
Reflecting on the support you provide to people every day will help you become more aware of their needs and more person centred in your day-to-day work. Keeping your reflections and looking back on them occasionally will help you to see how much you have developed.

▲ Supervision varies from workplace to workplace.

The purpose of supervision

The word 'supervision' can be off-putting, but the idea behind it is good. Supervision has a number of useful purposes. It:

- gives you the opportunity to discuss matters that are important to you
- is a time when you can ask for advice about, or help with, problems
- gives you the opportunity to make suggestions about how things might be changed or developed
- helps you identify symptoms of stress and take steps to reduce the causes of stress
- focuses on you, your work and your needs
- is a useful time to discuss your own development as a learning disability worker, career prospects and opportunities for training
- helps to build better teamwork because everyone has their own chance to talk things through in private
- helps staff morale because you know there is someone to listen and help deal with problems before they get out of hand
- highlights areas of good practice and identifies areas where practice can be improved
- can be used to set goals and plan activities.

How to get the most out of supervision

You should have regular supervision sessions with your line manager. Find out how often these sessions are and make every effort to attend them. If you are not having supervision sessions you should discuss this with your line manager and, if appropriate, the person responsible for human resources in your organisation.

The following will help you get the most out of your supervisions:

▲ It is important to get the most out of your supervision sessions.

- **Preparation.** Make a list of things you want to discuss and share it before the meeting. Your line manager will have a similar list and you can prepare an agenda for the session, in which you agree between you the order in which you want to discuss them. Any action that is agreed at the meeting should be recorded. Your organisation will have its own paperwork for recording supervision sessions. Progress should be discussed at the next session.

- **Reflection.** It's a good idea to get into the habit of thinking about your own practice. Your supervision meeting is a good place to reflect on the day-to-day support you provide. You will also need to do this when you work on your job plan and personal development plan.
- **Confidentiality.** It's the responsibility of both you and your line manager to ensure that discussions in supervision remain private and confidential.
- **Professionalism.** Act in a professional manner in the meeting. Supervision should not be used as an opportunity for you to moan about the people you support or your colleagues. If you have concerns about other people, raise them in a professional and constructive manner.
- **Honesty.** This is your opportunity to voice any concerns or problems that you have. If you don't raise them, you aren't giving your line manager an opportunity to support you.

Activity 7c

Supervision

Think about your last supervision session. Look back at the written record. What was valuable about it? How do you think you could get more out of it?

Share your views with your line manager.

Personal development plans

We make plans every day about what we need to do and how we are going to go about it. We may write some of these down. A personal development plan is a written plan in which you identify the knowledge and skills you need to develop, and devise an action plan to achieve them. You are not expected to do this on your own. Most organisations have a procedure for personal development planning and a document which you should complete with the help of your line manager.

The personal development process

While documentation varies between organisations, there are generally four stages to the personal development process:

- **Stage 1. Identifying your development needs.** This is the most difficult stage for some people. You will be asked to examine what you feel you are good at and what you need to improve. For example, 'I'm good at supporting Greg with his morning routine now and it all goes smoothly but I am still finding it hard to find out from him what he wants to do on the days he spends at home. I don't want to influence him.'

- **Stage 2. Action planning.** You need to set targets for building on your strengths and working on areas that you need to improve. For example, 'I need to be able to support Greg better with choice and decision-making and understand his likes and dislikes better.'

- **Stage 3. Implementing the plan.** Here you can identify what you need to do in order to meet your targets. You should monitor this regularly. In some organisations you will be asked to identify in your plan any courses you want to attend or qualifications you want to achieve. This is because your employer would like you to provide evidence of your commitment to achieving the qualification before they pay for the course, or claim funding. For example, 'When I have finished my induction I need to go on the course on person-centred working. I could also read books in the library on supporting choice.'

- **Stage 4. Reviewing the plan.** Reviewing is an important part of the personal development planning process. If it is to be effective, the plan should be a working document which you should look at regularly to keep track of how things are going, and assess whether the targets you set are still relevant and realistic. Your review forms the basis for the next personal development plan. For example, 'I have put into practice some of the lessons I learnt on the course and now understand what Greg likes and dislikes. This has helped me to support him better with day-to-day choices.'

A personal development plan should include a summary like this one.

Personal development plan		
Action	**Resources**	**When**
Attend manual handling training course	Next available course	10 December
Find out more about supporting people with epilepsy	Talk to manager of the service who is a specialist nurse	Before the end of September
Learn more about supporting people with their own medication	Ask Andy to provide me with ongoing support as I work with Harry while he learns to take his new epilepsy drugs	Ongoing during September

Involving people with learning disabilities in your personal development plan

The first stage of the process can often be the hardest. Sometimes it's easier to think of our weaknesses than our strengths, and it can be difficult to ask for and hear other people's opinions of how well we do our job. However, it's important to do this so we get a clear picture of our strengths and weaknesses.

Your line manager may well help you to do this as part of the process, but it's also a good idea to find out from the people you support how they see you. If they can communicate verbally, you could ask them to help you think about things you do well, or how you could do some things better. If they don't communicate verbally, you'll be able to tell how they feel about the way you support them by observing them. If you feel able to involve the people you support in your personal development plan, not only are you treating them with respect, but you will get a clear picture of how you are seen by the people who are central to your role.

When involving people with learning disabilities in discussing the support you provide and your development plans, you need to be aware of the power issues involved. Some people may find it easier to talk to someone else about these issues, not to you. If they prefer to be involved in this way you should respect their decision.

To demonstrate that you have understood the importance of gaining knowledge and skills in your role supporting an individual with a learning disability you should be able to discuss ways in which you can acquire both. The following example should help you do this.

Thinking point
If your friends or family say something good about you, how do you feel? How well do you respond to constructive criticism?

Example 7: Gaining knowledge and skills

Ayesha has recently started work for a care agency that provides personal assistants for children and adults with learning disabilities. Ayesha is an experienced care worker, but most of her experience is in nursing homes for older people. Ayesha starts work supporting twin teenage brothers Salim and Sadiq who live at home with their family. The brothers have profound learning disabilities and need a lot of support with their personal care, dressing and feeding in the mornings and then again in the afternoon and evening after school. Kerry is the senior worker in a team of six personal assistants who work with the brothers.

After working with Salim and Sadiq for four weeks, Kerry asks Ayesha to reflect on her experience so far and what she has learnt and asks her to prepare a draft personal development plan for her next supervision.

1. How do you think Ayesha should reflect on her experience over the last four weeks?
2. What could Ayesha do to prepare a draft personal development plan?

Now turn to the commentary on this example on page 80.

Commentaries on the examples

At the end of each chapter there is an example and a set of questions for you to answer. The commentaries below highlight the issues that you could have included in your answers. Not everything that can be said about the examples is included. This would take a chapter for each study on its own. They are designed only to act as guidelines on how to approach each situation, and examples of how you can use your own practical experiences to describe and comment on your day-to-day experiences.

If you are taking the Induction Award qualifications, you'll find that you are asked to describe situations and give examples using your own experience. Familiarity with working on examples will help you with this, although it is how you present and discuss your own practical experience that counts in the end.

Example 1: Policies and procedures

When she went to support Hannah that day, Maureen faced a number of challenges. She would need to help Hannah become calmer, so she could think through what might have happened to the ring. She needed to decide what course of action to take and later to help Hannah remain calm and relaxed while she talked to the police.

Maureen was correct to follow the procedure for reporting an incident. If Hannah had been alone the night before she could have assumed that she had mislaid the ring and that it would turn up eventually. However, because of Hannah's party there is a possibility that someone who was in the flat the night before may have taken it. If this was the case, Hannah needed to be aware that one of her 'friends' might be taking advantage of her. The incident reporting policy involved a visit from the police. Although this may have been distressing for Hannah, Maureen stayed with her throughout the interview to support her.

If Hannah had not wanted to report the incident, Maureen would have needed to explain to her that as a possible criminal offence had taken place, it was her job to do so. Hannah's right to confidentiality was not breached because the organisation's policy on confidentiality would have stated that confidentiality could be breached if a criminal offence was suspected. Maureen should have contacted her line manager if she was unsure of what action to take.

Example 2: Partnership working

In addition to his work with Lucy and Paul, Andrew worked with the benefits agency, the local bank and Lucy's family. He would also have kept his line manager updated about the situation and sought advice and support when he needed to. In supporting Lucy and Paul through this crisis, Andrew has used a variety of skills. He has communicated openly and clearly with everyone. He has behaved in a professional manner in his dealings with the benefits agency and the bank. He has worked sensitively with Lucy's family, understanding their concern for Lucy's well-being and recognising their expertise in relation to their daughter, while keeping Lucy's and Paul's rights to choose where they live as his priority.

Example 3: Professional relationships

There are a number of examples of poor practice in this example:

- Manjula and James should not gossip about other people they support, especially in public.
- Neither Manjula nor James communicates with Craig.
- James is going about his personal business during the time he is being paid to support Craig.
- Craig is not given a choice about which magazine he would like to buy.
- Craig is not given the opportunity to pay for the magazine or communicate with anyone in the shop.
- Craig's calm silence should not be taken to mean that he is happy – he may have very low expectations of the people who support him and take this treatment to be normal.
- The support Craig is being given cannot be described as person-centred. His visit to the shop was for the benefit of his support workers, not his own benefit.

Example 4: Factors that affect communication

Much of the evidence in the example points to the fact that, although those who support Karli think that it's a 'good thing' for her to go to college, Karli seems not to agree with them as things currently are. She does not want to take part in the activities that are on offer in the sessions because she engages with them only for a few minutes. She has learned that:

- if she goes to the toilet two or three times, she will miss quite a lot of the session

- if she hits someone, she will be able to stay at home for a few days and hitting out probably also releases some of her frustration at having to do something she does not like.

It might be that Karli enjoys coming to college but that she does not enjoy the course she is on. One way of finding something that Karli would enjoy more could be for her to have 'taster sessions' of other college activities and courses. Her support worker could observe her behaviour in these sessions to see if her concentration span is longer and whether she is happier in these sessions. If not, then Karli's own wishes should come before those of the people who support her, and they should help her find alternative activities.

Example 5: Communicating effectively

Wen could talk over with Benjamin what happened during the day. He might ask Benjamin to tell him about the waitress and how he feels about her. He must tell Benjamin that he will not be going back to the placement that week and why this is. He will need to explain why the waitress was upset and talk about appropriate ways of showing that you like someone.

Wen could use a variety of aids to help Benjamin understand the information, such as a calendar to show the days when Benjamin will not be going to the café and symbols or photographs showing emotions to illustrate how the waitress felt. He could also use these to find out how Benjamin is feeling.

Wen needs to ensure that the conversation with Benjamin takes place in private, in a place where Benjamin feels comfortable. He should ask Benjamin where he would prefer. He should check that Benjamin understands what is happening, give him time to respond and listen to him carefully, making sure that Benjamin knows he is listening. He should be aware that Benjamin may be angry and upset, and be prepared for ways in which he may express these emotions. However, Wen should not show any feelings of disappointment or anger about the way Benjamin has behaved.

Example 6: Record keeping

There are a number of areas of good practice in this example:

- The support plan is drawn up with the person.
- The organisation respects that individuals are in their own home and asks permission to keep their records there.

- The support worker ensures that the person understands what is being written about them in their home and the person signs it to show this has happened.
- People know about other records that are held about them, and the organisation makes them aware of their rights to see these documents at any time.

Example 7: Gaining knowledge and skills

Ayesha could reflect on her experiences over the last four weeks by using the Kolb's learning cycle. She could consider in detail two or three particular events or situations with the brothers, thinking about what had happened and seeking to understand what happened from different perspectives. Ayesha could use her wider understanding of supporting people and the knowledge she had gained from her NVQ to help her make sense of the situations. Ayesha could also use the ideas from her reflection to influence the day-to-day support she provides. Finally, Ayesha could ask the brothers' family if they feel that there is more Ayesha can learn about supporting them. Relatives appreciate being asked and can give a fresh perspective to the support provided.

In preparing a draft personal development plan, Ayesha could look at the organisation's paperwork for such plans. She could start to complete some sections, for example looking at her strengths and the areas she wants to improve. Ayesha could also seek input from the brothers and their family. Ayesha could start thinking about her action plan and how she would like to meet her development needs.

Glossary

advocate an independent person who supports someone to speak up for themselves

aims a general statement of what an organisation hopes to achieve

Code of Practice a UK document for social care workers setting out the standards they should be working to

confidentiality concerning things that need to be kept private

direct payments funding received direct from a local council so that people can organise their own social care support

family carer a relative of a person with learning disabilities who has an interest in their well-being

General Social Care Council the organisation that regulates the social care workforce in England and sets the standards of care through the Codes of Practice

individual budgets budgets that give individuals the ability to design their own social care support and the power to decide the nature of the services they need

induction a period of learning, shortly after starting a new job or volunteering placement, about how to provide good support to people with learning disabilities

job description a document that gives detailed information about your work, what you will be doing, who you are responsible to, etc.

person-centred approaches a way of working every day with people with learning disabilities that puts the person and their dreams at the centre of everything you do

policy a statement or plan of action that clearly sets out an organisation's position or approach on a particular issue and tells staff what should be done in the circumstances

procedures a set of instructions setting out in detail how a policy should be implemented and what staff should do in response to a specific situation

reflection careful consideration of ideas and issues

rights a framework of laws that protects people from harm and guarantees them basic entitlements, such as the right to respect, equality, and a fair trial

services the provision of social care support for a person that could be in their own home or elsewhere

support plan a detailed plan of a person's support needs that support workers should use to inform their day-to-day support for that individual

values what an organisation considers important in its work

Mapping to NVQ Health & Social Care Knowledge Specifications

Chapter 1: Understanding your job			
HSC23	**HSC24**		**HSC234**
1, 3, 5, 8, 9, 11	2, 8, 9, 11, 19		2, 3, 7, 8
HSC33	**HSC35**	**HSC3111**	**HSC3116**
1, 3, 4, 6, 7, 8, 9	1, 2, 4, 6, 7, 8, 11	1, 2, 4, 6, 7, 9, 11	3, 8, 12
Links to other units: HSC227, HSC233, HSC241, HSC387, HSC3100, HSC3114, HSC3119, HSC3121			

Chapter 2: Working in partnership					
HSC24		**HSC227**		**HSC234**	
2, 14, 20		3, 4, 12		3, 4	
HSC35	**HSC328**	**HSC329**	**HSC387**	**HSC3111**	**HSC3114**
2, 4, 9, 14, 15, 16, 22, 23	2, 4, 12, 13, 14	2, 3, 5, 14, 15, 16	3, 15, 20, 21, 22, 23, 24	2, 4, 15, 16, 17, 18, 20, 21	2, 3, 15, 16, 17
Links to other units: HSC21, HSC27, HSC233, HSC241, HSC31, HSC368, HSC3100, HSC3116, HSC3119					

Chapter 3: Your responsibilities as a support worker					
HSC24		**HSC27**	**HSC233**		**HSC234**
2, 3, 4, 6, 7, 8, 11, 15		1, 2, 3, 6, 7, 8, 10	1, 2, 3, 4, 6, 11		3, 4, 7
HSC35	**HSC328**	**HSC329**	**HSC335**	**HSC3111**	**HSC3114**
1, 2, 3, 4, 5, 6, 8, 14, 17	2, 3, 4, 5	2, 4, 5	2, 3, 5, 14, 21	1, 2, 3, 4, 6, 9, 18, 20	1, 2, 3, 4, 5, 14, 16, 17
Links to other units: HSC25, HSC3119					

Chapter 4: Factors that affect communication			
HSC21	**HSC24**		**HSC233**
2, 3, 7, 8, 9	2, 12		3, 9, 11
HSC31	**HSC35**	**HSC369**	**HSC370**
2, 3, 8, 9, 10, 11, 12, 13, 14, 15, 16	2, 16, 23	2, 4, 5, 15, 16, 17, 18, 19, 20, 21, 22, 25	4, 5, 16, 17, 18
Links to other units: HSC27, HSC336, HSC337, HSC371, HSC3111, HSC3114			

Chapter 5: Promoting effective communication

HSC21	HSC24	HSC233
1, 2, 3, 4, 6, 7, 8, 9	2, 6, 7	1, 3, 4, 6, 9, 11
HSC31	**HSC35**	**HSC369**
1, 2, 3, 9, 10, 11, 12, 13, 14, 15, 16	6, 16, 17, 23	1, 2, 3, 4, 5, 6, 7, 8, 16, 17, 18, 19, 20, 21, 22, 23, 24, 25
Links to other units: HSC234, HSC336, HSC370, HSC371, HSC3111		

Chapter 6: Keeping written records

HSC21	HSC24	HSC242
1, 4, 5, 10, 11, 12, 13, 14	2, 9, 21	1, 2, 3, 5, 6, 7, 8, 9
HSC31		
1, 4, 5, 17, 18, 19		
Links to other units: HSC25, HSC27, HSC233, HSC234, HSC35, HSC328, HSC329, HSC3111		

Chapter 7: Your personal development as a learning disability worker

HSC23
1, 2, 3, 4, 5, 6, 8, 9, 10,11, 12
HSC33
1, 2, 3, 4, 5, 6, 7, 8, 9, 11

Resources

Organisations

Social Care Councils in the UK and access to Codes of Practice for social care workers

The General Social Care Council is the social care council for England. Similar bodies exist in Wales, Scotland and Northern Ireland. The four councils were set up on 1 October 2001 under legislation to regulate the social care profession: the Care Standards Act 2000 in England and Wales; the Health and Personal Social Services Act 2001 in Northern Ireland; and the Regulation of Care (Scotland) Act 2001 in Scotland.

England
General Social Care Council
Goldings House
2 Hay's Lane
London SE1 2HB

Tel: 020 7397 5100 Fax: 020 7397 5101
Website: www.gscc.org.uk

Northern Ireland
Northern Ireland Social Care Council
7th Floor, Millennium House
Great Victoria Street
Belfast BT2 7AQ

Tel: 02890 417600 Fax: 02890 417601
Email: info@niscc.n-i.nhs.uk
Website: www.niscc.info

Scotland
Scottish Social Services Council
Compass House
Discovery Quay
11 Riverside Drive
Dundee DD1 4NY

Tel: 01382 207101 Fax: 01382 207215
Information service: 0845 6030891
Email: enquiries@sssc.uk.com
Website: www.sssc.uk.com

Wales
Care Council for Wales
6th Floor, West Wing
South Gate House
Wood Street
Cardiff CF10 1EW

Tel: 029 2022 6257 Fax: 029 2038 4764
Email: info@ccwales.org.uk
Website: www.ccwales.org.uk

Publications

Books on practice

Cambridge, P. and Carnaby, S. (eds) 2005. *Person Centred Planning and Care Management with People with Learning Disabilities.* London: Jessica Kingsley

Concannon, L. 2005. *Planning for Life: Involving adults with learning disabilities in service planning.* Abingdon: Routledge

Hollins, S. and Hollins, M. 2005. *You and Your Child: Making sense of learning disabilities.* London: Karnac Books

Mansell, J. 2004. *Person Centred Active Support.* Brighton: Pavilion

Books on supervision and personal development

Knapman, J. and Morrison, T. 1998. *Making the Most of Supervision in Health and Social Care: A support manual for supervisees in health and social care.* Brighton: Pavilion

Morrison, T. 2005. *Staff Supervision In Social Care: Making a real difference to staff and service users (3rd edn.).* Brighton: Pavilion

Books on communication

Grove, N. 2000. *See What I Mean.* Kidderminster: BILD

Lawton, A. 2006. *A Voice of their Own: A toolbox of ideas and information for non-instructed advocacy.* Kidderminster: BILD

Audio-visual

After Life. This 2004 film starring Paula Sage raises important issues about learning disabilities in society. www.sodapictures.com

Creative Conversations. A video aimed at supporting communication with people who have severe and profound learning disabilities. www.pavpub.com

My Home, My Rights, My Choices. A video, handbook and picture cards about making choices in everyday life. The Langstone Society (01384 243665)

Supported Living – Train the Trainers Pack. For training staff in supporting independent living. www.paradigm-uk.org

Useful websites

British Institute of Learning Disabilities: www.bild.org.uk
A charity that helps improve the life of people with a learning disability by providing services, events and publications for people with a learning disability and those who support them.

Circles Network: www.circlesnetwork.org.uk
A voluntary organisation providing information about person-centred planning and inclusion.

Communication Matters: www.communicationmatters.org.uk
A charity concerned with augmentive and alternative communication.

The Department of Health: www.dh.gov.uk
Health and social care policy, guidance and publications.

Foundation for People with Learning Disabilities: www.learningdisabilities.org.uk
A charity that promotes the rights, quality of life and opportunities of people with learning disabilities and their families.

General Social Care Council:
    www.gscc.org.uk (England)
    www.niscc.info (Northern Ireland)
    www.sssc.uk.com (Scotland
    www.ccwales.org.uk (Wales

Makaton: www.makaton.org
A sign language support system for people with learning disabilities.

Mencap: www.mencap.org.uk
A charity providing services for, and also campaigning and lobbying with, people with learning disabilities.

National Family Carer Network: www.familycarers.org.uk

Office of Public Sector Information: www.opsi.gov.uk
includes information about Acts of Parliament

People First: www.peoplefirst.org.uk
An advocacy organisation run by people with learning disabilities.

Signalong: www.signalong.org.uk
A sign language support system for people with learning disabilities.

Index